For Nina with love x – James Campbell

For Uncle Norman – Rob Jones

BLOOMSBURY CHILDREN'S BOOKS
Bloomsbury Publishing Plc
50 Bedford Square, London, WC1B 3DP, UK

BLOOMSBURY, BLOOMSBURY CHILDREN'S BOOKS and the Diana logo are trademarks
of Bloomsbury Publishing Plc

First published in Great Britain 2019 by Bloomsbury Publishing Plc

A catalogue record for this book is available from the British Library

ISBN: 978-1-4088-9824-6

4 6 8 10 9 7 5 3

Printed and bound in Great Britain by CPI (UK) Ltd, Croydon CR0 4YY

To find out more about our authors and books visit www.bloomsbury.com
and sign up for our newsletters

The author and publisher recommend enabling SafeSearch when using the Internet in conjunction with
this book. We can accept no responsibility for information published on the Internet.

THE FUNNY LIFE OF TEACHERS

JAMES CAMPBELL

ROB JONES

BLOOMSBURY
CHILDREN'S BOOKS
LONDON OXFORD NEW YORK NEW DELHI SYDNEY

STOP

Read this before you dare go any further ...

Fact ⚠ WARNING ⚠ WARNING ⚠ Fact ▷

◁ Fact ⚠ WARNING ⚠ WARNING ⚠ Fact ▷

Your teachers will NOT enjoy reading this. Anything you think you might learn from this book might not be very accurate so should not be used in a school project or as part of your homework. Unless, of course, you are made from the colours of the moon and are as brave as forever.

Fact Alert

Fact Alert

WHAT SORT OF BOOK IS THIS?

This is not a fact book as such. You won't find much practical information in here.

If you're looking for **proper** educational stuff about **teachers** and **school** then put this book down immediately and run away screaming. If it's **practical** information you really want, I can recommend the following books:

This book is for four types of people:

1. People who go to some sort of school and like reading about how funny and ridiculous teachers are.

2. People who used to go to school and were so scarred by the experience that they still have nightmares. This book might help.
OR MAKE IT WORSE.

3. People who are about to go to school, or start a new school, for the **first time.** This book will help you work out what to expect and stop your knees knocking together as you walk through the door.

4. People who have never been to school, never met a teacher, don't care a rotten banana about teachers but like laughing until their ears go blue and their wellies fly off.

There is only one category of people who should **NOT** read this book. That is ... **TEACHERS!**

If you see a teacher reading this book, point to the middle distance and yell, 'Look! Bears are attacking!' and **steal** the book from them while they're looking the other way. Teachers must **not** be allowed to read this book under any circumstances.

You don't read this book like a **normal book,** by starting on page 1 and then reading all the other pages in the right order.

BORING!

You can read this book forwards, backwards, sidewards, upwards, downwards, wearing a **banana suit** and in approximately **65,537** different ways. To choose a path just turn to the page the signpost says.

Some pages have **'back' signposts,** which tell you how to get back to where you came from. Sometimes there is more than one way to get to that page. When this happens you can either choose to go back to where you actually came from or go back to somewhere you've never been before.

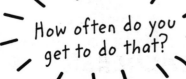
How often do you get to do that?

This book will make you laugh about how funny teachers can be until snot comes out of your nose. It will also help you to understand these strange creatures and their natural habitat: **school.**

Most teachers live in **strange buildings** where everything is labelled, bells go off at specific times and there are **rules** that don't exist anywhere else in the universe, like:

> Don't run in the corridors
> Sit on your bottoms
> Don't lick other people's faces*

Some teachers seem quite friendly but then write all over your work in **red pen.** Other teachers spend most of their time staring out the window and you have to give them a nudge and remind them to teach you. Other teachers are **so wonderful** that they will change your life – and then do a weird dance that makes you feel sick.

Let's dance!

*Generally speaking it's not a good idea to lick anyone's face out of school either – unless they have chocolate on their cheeks.

A warning about facts

Occasionally, this book will give you some **actual facts.**

Recorders are a really popular instrument in schools. Go online and you will discover that the Internet agrees with this. But is it really true?

You have to be **careful** with facts. Facts change all the time. In twenty years' time when you give this book to your own children, half of the facts in this book will be **wrong.** However, all of the fictional things in this book will still be **true** until the rings of Saturn come round to your house for a cup of tea.

Beginning page

Congratulations on making it to the beginning of the book. Some people don't make it this far without stubbing their toe.

Decide which page you would like to start with. **Remember:** there is no right or wrong way to read this book!

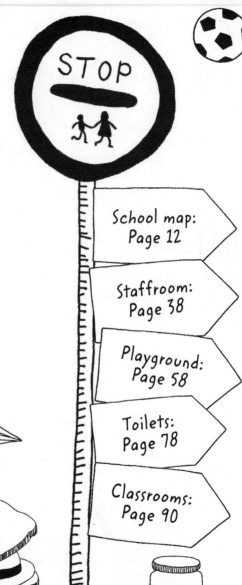

Teacher's Bottom Burps

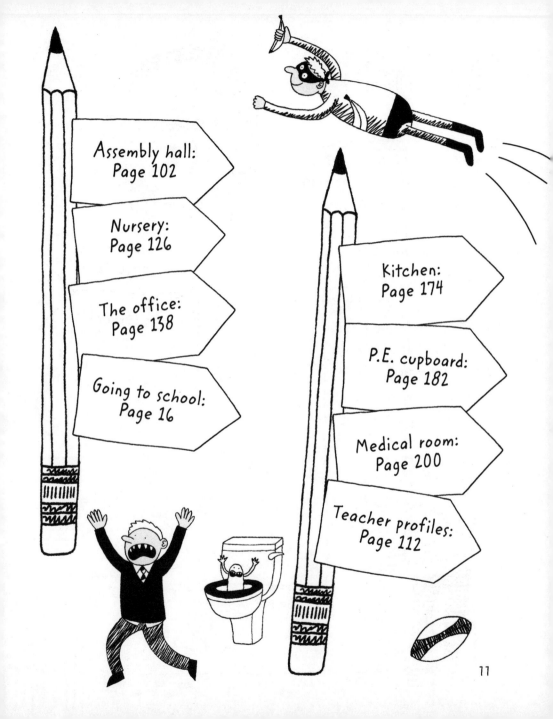

School map

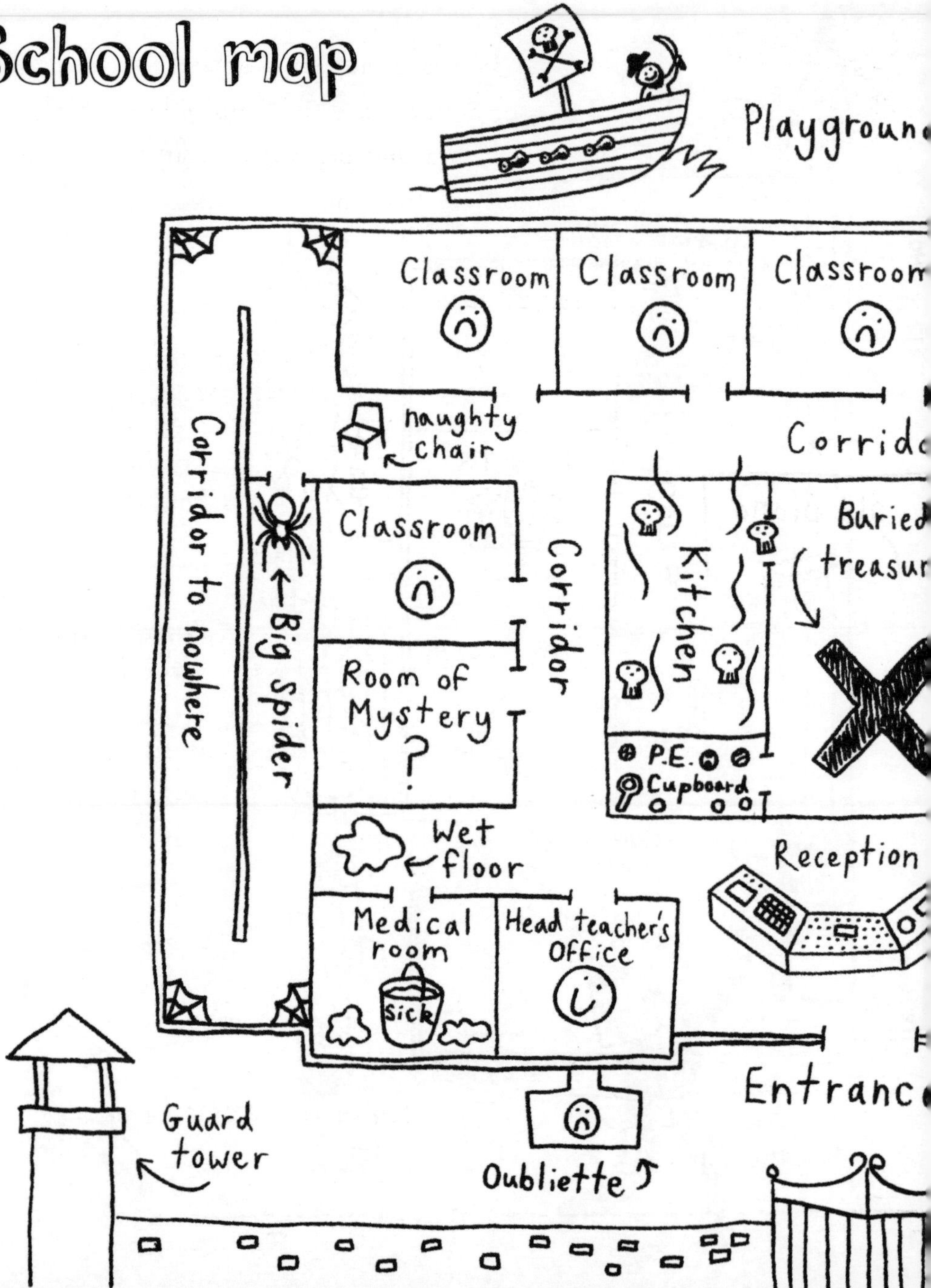

Playground

Classroom

Classroom

Classroom

naughty chair

Corridor

Corridor to nowhere

← Big Spider

Classroom

Corridor

Kitchen

Buried treasure

Room of Mystery ?

P.E. Cupboard

Wet floor

Medical room

sick

Head teacher's Office

Reception

Guard tower

Oubliette ↰

Entrance

Here is a map of a school I have made up. Schools are the natural habitat of teachers and are where you will find them most of the time.

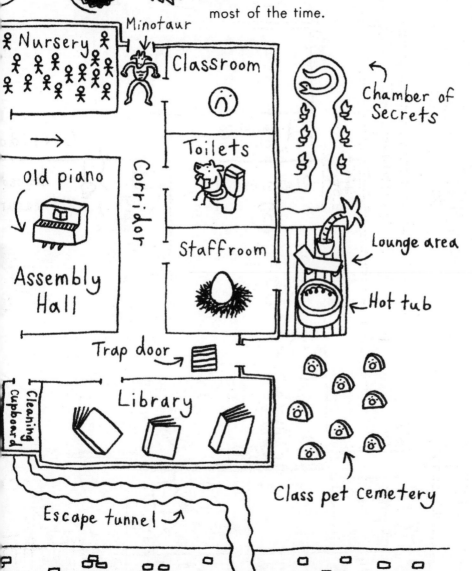

Nursery

Minotaur

Classroom

Chamber of Secrets

Old piano

Corridor

Toilets

Assembly Hall

Staffroom

Lounge area

Hot tub

Trap door

Cleaning Cupboard

Library

Class pet cemetery

Escape tunnel

Different types of teacher and where to find them

There are many different types of teacher. Some are very **thin** and some are very **wide.** Some have recently arrived from another planet and want you to take them to your leader. Then you find out that they are your **leader** and you have to take them to themselves, which can be very confusing – especially when you're in the middle of trying to finish a history project.

Teacher profiles: Page 112

The natural habitat of teachers is a **school.**

Some schools are for tiny children, others are for **huge** children. Some are for children with jelly in their slippers. Others are for children with six legs. Oh no. Hang on, I'm thinking of ants.

The buildings are **different** too.

Forest schools: Page 96

Some are brand new and it feels like you're in an airport. Others are old and have been there for hundreds of years. The walls are made of stone and you feel a bit like you're in a church. Some schools are **cosy and warm.** Other schools are outside! Most schools are places you go to in the morning and leave at the end of the afternoon. Other schools have bedrooms and you stay over night with loads of other children.

How teachers get to school: Page 24

Teachers through time: Page 36

Primary schools: Page 48

Boarding schools: Page 80

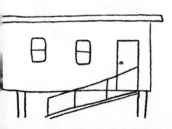

Going to school

Why am I even here?

There are lots of ways to get to school. Most ways include **wheels.** But they almost never include a duck wearing glasses.

ON A SCOOTER

Going to school on a scooter is **brilliant** and **rubbish** at the same time. There should be a word for that: **rubbliant** or **brillyish**.

It's **brilliant** because you get to ride on your scooter. You can travel faster than the speed of light and they make a great noise as they whizz along.

WAAAAAAA AAAIIIIIIITTTTTTTT! IT'S DANGEROOOO OOUSSSSSSSS!

It's **rubbish** because you have to keep waiting for your grown-up at the roads. There you are, cruising along the pavement, the morning sun pouring goodness on to your face. You are free, free, freeeee. Until you hear this ...

When you get to school, there is usually a scooter garage where you can park your scooter. Often, a **fat Labrador** has been tied to this. Apparently, he is there because dogs are not allowed in the playground in case they do a poo. But I like to think of him as the:

Guardian of the Scooters.

Hand over the scooter and nobody gets hurt.

When do scooters need defending? Because cats steal them and sell them to scrap metal dealers for jars of **fish paste!**

IN A CAR

Some people live **too far** from school to walk so they get driven by grown-ups. This can be a joyful experience as you all listen to the radio together and talk about what is going to happen in your day. That is if you're on time. If you're running late, going to school in a car is more like being a tin box full of **shoutiness** and **stress.**

The best thing about being in a car is going over speed bumps. These are obstacles put there to make your journey more like a **roller coaster.** If you're running on time, speed bumps will make you do an amusing bounce – a bit like doing a hiccup.

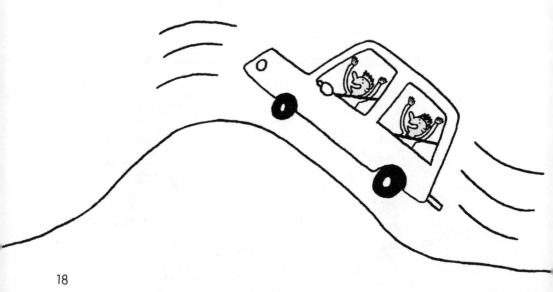

If you're running late, a **speed bump** can be more like being catapulted over a mountain. Some grown-ups go so fast over a speed bump that you'll have to hold on to your little brother to stop him banging his head off the roof.

The downside to be driven to school is that it's not great for the environment. Unless of course, your car is **pedal powered.** You can drive a pedal-powered car as much as you like without damaging the planet at all.

If you live in a town or city, another problem you will almost certainly have is **traffic jams.** But I have invented a solution for this. It doesn't use any oil and there are no traffic issues. Simply get yourself **catapulted** to school!

Slingshot effect: Page 72

What the flickering pilchard are we going to do about it?: Page 170

Catapulting to school: Page 134

ON THE BUS

In some places, there is a **school bus** to take children to school. Only children are allowed on the bus and it picks up kids from their houses or the corners of roads in the middle of nowhere. The school bus is usually extremely old and may break down a lot. The school **bus driver** is also usually extremely old and may break down a lot.

I think my oils are leaking again ...

If you're lucky enough to get the bus to school, you will find it's a **great place** to do your homework, make friends, sing songs and play badminton.

My favourite kind of bus is the **walking bus.** This is when some grown-up volunteers guide a group of children to walk to school in one big safe lump, stopping to pick up people on the way. Sometimes they all **hold hands.** Sometimes they hold on to a **rope.** When you're coming up to your stop, simply **squeeze** the nose of the person next to you. The driver will hear them **scream** and know to pull over.

I think this is a **great way** to get to school and grown-ups should do it too!

Being late:
Page 84

ON A BIKE

One of the most **fun ways** to get to school is on a **bike.** It's also one of the most dangerous. It's the only way of getting to school that involves you being **in charge** and on the road.

You are in charge

On the road

Neither

I used to cycle to school and once I had an accident. It was a very windy day. In fact, there was a **hurricane!** I was fighting against the wind, when my foot slipped off the pedal and my heel went into the spokes of my front wheel.

I went flying over the handlebars and then got **run over** by my *own* bike.

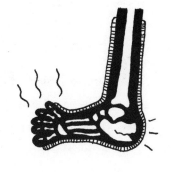

I broke my heel and had to spend six weeks on crutches with my foot in plaster. On that plaster I wrote my first really **bad poem.**

I WAS RIDING MY BIKE ON A WINDY DAY
AND I WAS NEARLY BLOWN OFF.
I PUT MY HEEL
INSIDE THE WHEEL
AND CHIPPED A PIECE OF BONE OFF!

Going to school: Page 16

HOW TEACHERS GET TO SCHOOL

Obviously, most teachers don't need to travel backwards and forwards to school because **THEY LIVE THERE.** You can find them curled up somewhere in the classroom, usually in the corner of the carpet area. Or sometimes at night they gather with other teachers in the staffroom; some hanging from the ceiling like **bats** and the rest burrowed in a pile of cardigans and sensible shoes.

Snacks

Learning makes you **hungry.** Running around makes you hungry. In fact, when you're a child, just sitting around doing nothing can make you hungry. Because of this you need **snacks.** If you don't have snacks, your head will go all wobbly and you'll fall over.

When I visit schools now, I always carry an **emergency banana** in my bag.

Emergency banana

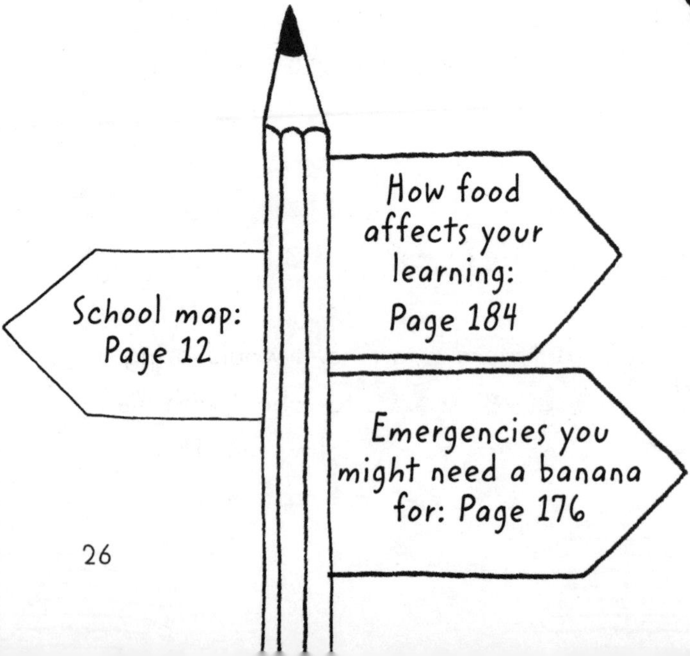

School map: Page 12

How food affects your learning: Page 184

Emergencies you might need a banana for: Page 176

Most schools have a break in the morning and that's when you eat your snack. A snack is usually a **piece of fruit.** You can bring other types of food in if you like but you would look weird if you brought in a full **roast dinner.**

Put that emergency banana away or the goat will get you!

Teachers need snacks too. There is usually a big box of **chocolates** in the staffroom because it was someone's birthday. Or if not, someone will run out and get a **GIANT BOX** of doughnuts.

If I were a teacher I would bring a **live goat** to school with me and use its milk in my tea. This is exactly why I am **not** a teacher.

House points

These are points that teachers award you for doing good things at school – like writing an **excellent story**, knowing something that no one else did or not wetting yourself when the lollipop lady growled at you.

But you don't get to keep these points. They get added to the total of all the other points given to pupils who are in the same house as you. At the end of the term whichever house has the most points is the **winner** of the competition and they usually get a trophy or a badge or a **bunch of bananas** or something.

Congratulations!

Lunchtime:
Page 52

Things that
shouldn't be in
this book:
Page 204

Reception:
Page 34

Wouldn't it be fun if teachers took **ideas** from books and started using them in schools? When I was at school, my favourite book was *Alice In Wonderland* and the best bit was the Mad Hatter's Tea Party. I would have **loved** it if at lunchtime we had to keep moving one place to the left every couple of minutes. That way you would get bits of **other** people's packed lunch!

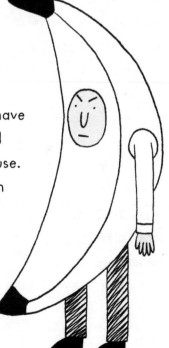

Teachers belong to houses too and they have to be very careful not to be **biased** and give loads of house points to their own house. If they do that, the head teacher will punish them by making them wear a **banana costume** all day for a whole week.

How teachers
motivate you:
Page 94

Frogspawn story

When I was about ten, I had a **brilliant idea!** We had a pond in our back garden full of **frogspawn.** I decided that everyone at school would be really impressed if I brought it in so we could watch it turn into **tadpoles.**

My teacher said it was a great idea but wondered how I would **transport** the tadpoles to school. I said we had an old goldfish bowl. He said that a bowl full of tadpoles and pond water would be very **heavy** and didn't think I'd get all the way to school without dropping it. Obviously, I decided that he was completely **wrong** and the next day I set off to school with my bowl of frogspawn.

After about five minutes, I realised my teacher was right! The bowl was really **heavy,** smooth and wet so it was hard to hold on to.

Things that were normal for your parents: Page 196

And then ... I stumbled on the footpath edge. I didn't fall on my face but I did go a bit wobbly and the water in the bowl wobbled too. **PLOP.** A tiny piece of frogspawn fell out and landed **splat** on the footpath.

It was only a tiny amount and I had millions of **gloopy blobs** left. But as I carried on, all I could think about was the bit I'd left behind. 'They will never turn into tadpoles. They will never be happy frogs. Because I have **MURDERED** them!'

I started to **cry.** I couldn't work out how to put the bowl down to wipe my eyes so I carried on walking with my eyes full of tears. I couldn't see where I was going so **I tripped again.** And this time a great **big** blob of frogspawn landed on the street. Now I was really crying. I was a **tadpole murderer!**

The more I **cried,** the more I couldn't see. The more I couldn't see, the more I tripped. The more I tripped, the more I spilled. The more I spilled, the more I cried. And so it went on and on **and on.**

Oh no! I've lost some frogspawn.

By the time I got to school I had an **empty goldfish bowl** and a trail of dying frogspawn behind me. I'm not sure what the moral of this story is. **Maybe ...**

LEAVE FROGSPAWN ALONE!

The Airedale Air Museum

The Airedale Air Museum mostly consists of **air** and is possibly the most **boring** museum in the world. Not just any air, mind you, but air from different parts of history, all **sealed up** in jars.

The least boring part is the **Last Breath gallery**, which houses the last breaths of various historical figures. You can see the last breath of people such as **Shakespeare** and **Cleopatra.**

Cleopatra's
Last
Breath

Shakespeare's
Last
Breath

Toilets:
Page 78

The second least boring part is the room dedicated to the Airedale Terrier, the world's only **inflatable dog.** It's a great place to hire for a birthday party.

Most recently, however, the Airedale Air Museum has opened up a new exhibition called **Teachers Through Time,** which tells a reasonably interesting story. It includes a Victorian school room, a digital school room from the future and even an actual teacher called Mrs Fridgewater who sits very still **while** stealthily releasing **bottom burps** which the museum collects and put in jars.

Teacher's Bottom Burps

33

Reception

I am **very lucky** to have travelled to lots of schools around the world but most of the thousands of schools I have visited have been in the UK. And almost all of those schools have a very **confusing** sign in the car park ...

ALL VISITORS
MUST REPORT
TO RECEPTION

The problem is that there are **two types** of reception in most UK primary schools. There's the one the secretary hangs out in and then there is Reception – the first year of primary school. The hours I have wasted going to the **wrong one.**

Hello. I'm here to report to you.

Are you my imaginary friend?

No.

I have chicken pox.

It's not the sort of reception I was looking for. Smearing your name on my face with **snot** is not the same as giving someone a visitor's badge.

The office: Page 138

Other parts of the world call the **first year** of school completely different things. In some parts of the UK, they have stopped calling it Reception and are calling it **Foundation** (which I'm sure is something my mum puts on her face when she's going out).

In Australia, the first year of school is called **Prep.** That's short for 'preparing for school'. I don't see how they are preparing for school. All they do is play with sand. Maybe they are preparing to go to school in the desert.

In New Zealand, they call it **Year Zero.**

What year are you in at school?

I'm in Nothing. Nothing at all. Next year I'm going to be Something.

Teachers through time

In Stone Age times, children went to school in a **cave.** The teachers at this time were very hairy and mostly **grunted** at their students. You might be surprised to know that cavemen did actually have an **alphabet.**

A	= ug	J	= erm	S	= I've-got-a-lovely-bunch-of-bananas
B	= ugg	K	= aah	T	= mump
C	= urg	L	= aaah	U	= bump
D	= urgg	M	= sausage	V	= wump
E	= uug	N	= urp	W	= stig
F	= uuurg	O	= gurpp	X	= stug
G	= uugg	P	= burp	Y	= pug
H	= oof	Q	= weewee	Z	= ooh-I-think-I-left-the-iron-on
I	= ooff	R	= fluuuuurm		

In Ancient Egypt, teachers were usually cats. The best history teachers would be ones who actually have the ability to travel **backwards and forwards** in time. Then you could ask them what it was like in Roman times or during the **American Civil War.**

Having said that, some teachers look so old that they can **actually** remember what it was like **two hundred years** ago because they were alive then.

The Airedale Air Museum: Page 32

Teacher profiles: Page 112

Punishments: Page 120

Staffroom

The **staffroom** is the inner sanctum of the teachers' habitat. This is where they eat, rest and exchange information with one another.

As a rule, you **shouldn't** go in the staffroom but sometimes a teacher might ask you to go in there for one of the following reasons:

1. You've been asked to tell the teachers that break time is **over.**

2. You've done **something wrong** and need to find a teacher to tell you off.

3. You've done something **so well** that you have been promoted to teacher.

You must never just walk into the staffroom. You must always **knock on the door** and then wait. Why is this? Well, because the teachers might be in the middle of doing something private and important. Like playing

Twister.

Staffrooms are usually small with no windows and smell like old coffee. They are best avoided but if you **really** want to find out more about them, go here ...

What teachers talk about in the staffroom:
Page 40

Things on the staffroom wall:
Page 42

What teachers talk about in the staffroom

I have written this for you in the form of a **play** that you and your friends can perform together. This is a typical **conversation** that I have heard in one of the two and a half thousand staff rooms I have been in.

NARRATOR: Welcome to the staffroom. This is where our teachers relax between lessons, drink coffee and discuss different challenges and plans for educating your rapidly expanding brains. Let's hear what they are talking about today ...

Young teacher

Old teacher

OLD TEACHER: Did you watch anything exciting on the television last night?

Staffroom: Page 38

YOUNG TEACHER: Yes. I watched that baking programme.

OLD TEACHER: The one where they bake the cakes?

YOUNG TEACHER: Yes. Did you see it?

Narrator

OLD TEACHER: No. I've never seen it.

YOUNG TEACHER: What did you do then?

OLD TEACHER: I spent three hours trying to work out how to put salt in my dishwasher.

YOUNG TEACHER: Why do you put salt in your dishwasher? I've been putting pepper in mine.

NARRATOR: Crikey, this is boring. Could you two just stop talking please? I'm going home.

THE END.

Things on the staffroom wall

The staffroom wall is a **fascinating** place. If you ever find yourself in the staffroom of your school, make sure you get a **good look** at all the things that are on it. If you're lucky, you will see **announcements** of babies, details of Christmas parties and cries for help like:

Does anyone know how to work the digital camera? :(

I'm looking for 5,000 empty yoghurt pots can anyone help?

My arm-pit's ON FIRE!

Allergy children: Page 86

Who has taken all the felt?: Page 44

Staffroom: Page 38

Art: Page 172

Sometimes, teachers put really **good examples** of your work on the wall in the staffroom to show off to all the other teachers what a brilliant teacher they are.

Sometimes, the staffroom wall also includes pictures of children with **allergies** or **illnesses.**

The **best thing** I've ever seen on a staffroom wall was written in thick red pen on a whiteboard. It simply said:

WHO HAS TAKEN ALL THE FELT?!..

Educational Trip to Legless Larry's Wine Bar this Friday. Sign up below.

Who has taken all the felt?

The **best thing** I've ever seen on a staffroom wall was written in thick red pen on a whiteboard. I was sitting there waiting for my next session, drinking a nice cup of tea. I looked up and someone had written:

> WHO HAS TAKEN
> ALL THE FELT?!

Catapulting to school: Page 134

Things on the staffroom wall: Page 42

Who wrote this message? It must have been a really angry head teacher. 'I am so cross,' she must have said to herself. 'I will write this in red pen. I just want to find out who has taken ALL of the felt.'

Then I thought, why does it say **ALL the felt?** How much felt are we talking about? A primary school probably gets through a lot of felt. So how much is **ALL** the felt?

Is there a **felt cupboard** in the storeroom that is supposed to be full of all different types and colours of felt? Or has one teacher been ordering massive amounts of felt without permission and then it's all just been **disappearing?**

Did a **lorry load** of felt turn up the day before and deliver **27 tonnes** of felt? Did they have to store this felt in all sort of weird places, like the assembly hall, the library and even inside the kettle? Was there a giant **felt mountain** in the middle of the playground with children bouncing on it like a **felty trampoline?**

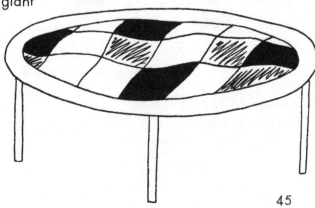

And now, has all that felt **simply vanished?** The head teacher has spent millions of pounds on felt and now it's all gone. And that's why she has written in really **angry red pen.**

WHO HAS TAKEN ALL THE FELT?!

There is no money left for pencils or recorders. Because somebody has **spent it all** on felt. And now the felt has vanished!

Maybe one teacher really likes felt. He wears a **felt suit** and makes all the children in his class wear pointy felt hats. All of his lessons are about felt. All of his topics are about felt.

Head teachers: Page 144

One day the head teacher will suspect something and storm into his classroom to see all the desks and walls covered in felt, all the children covered in felt and this teacher dressed in a **giant felt ball gown** ruffling all around him like a glorious felty cake. And the head teacher will say, 'Did YOU take ALL the felt?' And he will say:

> I have literally no idea what you are talking about.

Because he is a ...

FELT MONSTER!

Primary schools

People go to primary schools between the ages of four and eleven. They are put into **classes,** looked after by a teacher and sometimes a teaching assistant. Most of the time they stay with this one teacher who teaches them all their lessons. They might go to a different teacher occasionally for certain lessons like music, P.E. and **jelly-sculpting.**

Primary schools do things like **sports days** and **school plays.** They are warm, **cosy places** to be and everything is labelled.

The teachers in primary schools are generally warm and cosy people. A bit like **human teapots.** I like primary schools.

Teacher profiles: Page 112

Secondary schools

When you go to secondary school the teachers usually specialise in teaching one subject like Maths, Science or **Tobogganing.**

At the beginning of secondary school you will be given a **map** of the school and a timetable. Lose this as quickly as possible! That way you can have lots of fun being **late** and wandering into the wrong classroom.

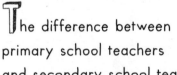

The difference between primary school teachers and secondary school teachers are **numerous ...**

Primary school teachers have more yoghurt on their clothes.

Secondary school teachers are more likely to be afraid of sharks.

Primary school teachers often have little patterns on one side of their face from sleeping in the carpet area.

Science

Science teachers are like **inventors** and **mad doctors** rolled into one. The best ones love finding out how things work and helping you find out too. They drink their coffee from a conical flask and often do **experiments** on their cat.

In **science lessons** you will learn all sorts of things about how the world works. This can cover a variety of stuff including why volcanoes erupt, why it rains, what tadpoles turn into and why we really need to **stop** chopping down the rainforest.

The water cycle:
Page 169

As you get older you will also get to use things like **Bunsen burners** which are basically tiny flame throwers. You'll even get to see what the inside of a frog looks like.

Some of the really **cool things** in science, however, don't seem to get taught very much. If you're interested I've written a couple of lessons about these things ...

You can come through now, Froggy.

Slingshot effect: Page 72

Quantum physics: Page 82

Things they don't teach you in school: Page 76

Lunchtime

The **worst thing** about being a teacher is having to eat your lunch in the dinner hall with all the children. It's a teacher's job to make sure that everyone **behaves** themselves and it's very difficult to do this whilst digesting a cheese and pickle sandwich.

Some people really like school lunches. Other people would rather die and actually prefer to get their grown-ups to make a packed lunch for them.

This is a bit like a **picnic** except that, rather than eating your lunch in a field painted with sunshine and surrounded by nature, you'll be eating it in a **noisy hall** surrounded by hundreds of screaming, chomping and burping other children probably being **splattered** by whatever **awfulness** they are consuming.

The most **common** thing in a packed lunch is a **sandwich.** This is two pieces of bread, usually buttered and filled with flat things you can eat. Some foods go well in a sandwich: ham, cheese and beef for example. Some things do not go well in a sandwich: hats, hamsters and **hairbrushes** for example.

You might also get a packet of crisps and some fruit in your packed lunch. Tiny packets of raisins that look like **rabbit droppings** are popular too.

The best grown-ups will write you **special notes** and put them in your packed lunch box. These can be soppy, inspirational or just plain weird. For example:

> We love you even more when you're not with us.

> You are made of stardust. Shine in all your lessons today!

> When I was your age, I ate shoes at lunchtime.

Kitchen: Page 174

School dinners: Page 122

Accidentally calling your teacher mum: Page 149

Recorders

Do you play the **recorder?** If so – **WHY?** It sounds **terrible.** It's not a musical instrument. It's an instrument of torture. Once you leave school, you'll never see a recorder ever again. They don't **exist** in the real world. You don't switch on the radio to hear:

Here is the latest single from Katy Perry – ON THE RECORDER!

And why are they called recorders? They don't record anything. There isn't a **red button** to record the beautiful music they produce. That's because they sound like a **parrot** going through a shredder.

𝒴our recorder teacher is usually **so old** that they have gone deaf. This is the only way that anyone can teach the recorder – by not being able to hear the **horrible noise** that they make!

STOP

Attack of the wasp: Page 150

Things that you only see in schools: Page 156

School council

The school council is a group of pupils who are **elected** by their **classmates** to talk about things that affect the children of the school like what the playground should look like, what colour the carpet area should be in the reception classroom and who has taken all of the felt!

To get on the school council you have to get **more votes** than anyone else in your class.

VOTE FOR ME

VOTE

Sports day: Page 88

There are two **main ways** to do this:

1. Have lots of **friends,** be nice to everyone and ask them to vote for you because they like you.

2. Convince everyone that the way things have been going up until now have been **terrible** and it has to be **stopped. Scare** them into thinking that they need to change things and explain that you are the **only** person who can do this. Then, once elected, realise that you have **no idea** what you are doing.

One of my children got elected to the **school council** once – using the first technique – but got a little bit confused about what he was supposed to do. He told me that it was now his job to watch out for **naughty children** when the teacher wasn't there and punish them himself. I think he may have got confused between the school council and Batman.

BATMAN

If you get on to your school council maybe think about how you can make the school **better.** Improving school lunches is often a good way to start. No one learns anything when they are hungry ...

How food affects your learning: Page 184

Playground

Children's bodies aren't really designed for sitting at desks. They are designed for **swinging** from bars and **jumping** around. Playgrounds are a place where you can blow off steam. They are also a place you can blow off **bottom burps.**

Nursery school playgrounds might just be like a garden with loads of toys. As you get older you might get some playground equipment like a slide and things to climb on. Once you get to be a grown-up there are no playgrounds at all! Teachers usually just have to stand around a **kettle** talking about what was on the telly last night.

Sometimes they are really **lucky** and get to do something called 'playground duty'. This is when they stand in the middle of the playground and shout at children who are enjoying themselves too much. What teachers would **REALLY** love is if they could join in with your **games.**

You should ask them if they would like to play too. Most teachers are particularly good at pretending to **fly.**

Many exciting things happen at break time. Epic football matches are won and lost. **Accidents** happen, bones are broken and **friendships** are made. The playground can also be an amazingly **creative** place. When you are playing imagination games like pretending to be a dragon or a princess or a marmalade cow, you might not be using a pen but you're still making up **stories.**

I'm not allowed to run around the playground being a dragon any more. I'm **too old.**

Accidents at school: Page 202

Playground games: Page 62

Playground assistants: Page 68

Different sizes of cow

I have a **theory** that different-sized cows produce different types of milk. Whole milk comes from a **normal-sized** cow. Semi-skimmed milk comes from miniature Shetland Cows, which are about the same size as a **Great Dane.**

Skimmed milk comes from **teeny tiny cows** the size of hamsters.

hamster

Or maybe they **skim** the cow? Across a lake. Like a pebble.

Lunchtime:
Page 52

Maybe you can get tiny **microscopic cows** the size of bacteria. What would they produce if you could milk them?

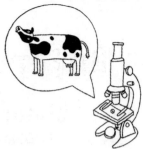

They would probably just make **water.** That's probably where water comes from. There are billions of microscopic cows floating around in the sky making **clouds.** And then birds fly through these clouds and accidentally milk them with their feathers as they fly. This causes water to fall out as **rain.** So the rain is really just very, very **weak milk.** The rain then lies around in lakes and puddles until it evaporates into evaporated milk ...

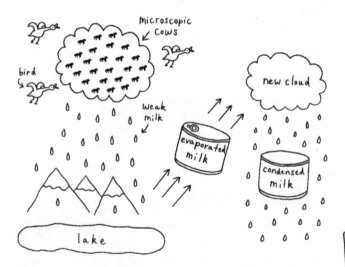

... the evaporated milk floats up back into new clouds where it either gets milked again or turns into **condensed milk!**

And **that** is the **water cycle.**

The water cycle: Page 169

Playground games

The most **interesting** thing about playground games is that the games are **passed down** from generation to generation. Some of my **favourite** playground games are:

Playground: Page 58

- *Fishy Wishy Fish*
- *It*
- *Walking around on your own*
- *Talking to yourself about trains*

In **Fishy Wishy Fish** you have to go up to someone and say without laughing, 'I'm a fishy wishy fish. I wish my wishy fishy wish was you.' And they have to say, 'I wish your fishy wishy fish was as fishy and wishy as a fishy wishy wish fish.' Usually by the time you've done this without **laughing,** the bell has gone and playtime is over. These days I play this game with my dog. She's rubbish at it as she doesn't know how to make a **shh** sound.

I love you

62

IT is a simple game in where you run around trying to touch each other. It's a great way to **spread diseases.** When I was at school I gave seven children chicken pox like this.

Some really old playground games are recorded in the Airedale Air Museum. These include *Jump the Plague Pit* and *How to make an Egyptian Mummy.* I'm sure you can work out the **rules** for these games yourselves. Or make them up. If you do please let me know by emailing:

ireallycouldnotcareless@pleasegoaway.com

The Airedale Air Museum: Page 32

How to tell which way is north

If you ever **get lost** in the middle of the desert, the middle of the jungle or the middle of the school field, it can be very handy to know which way is **north.** If you know which way is north you can **navigate** yourself around a map, make sure you are going in the right direction and, eventually, make your way to the **North Pole.**

The most **reliable** way to know which way is north is to use a **compass.** A compass has a needle which wobbles around and then points to the North Pole. If you want to go north, follow the **red end.** If you want to go south, go the opposite way. If you want to go a different way then you need to learn how to work a compass properly and maybe learn some **trigonometry.**

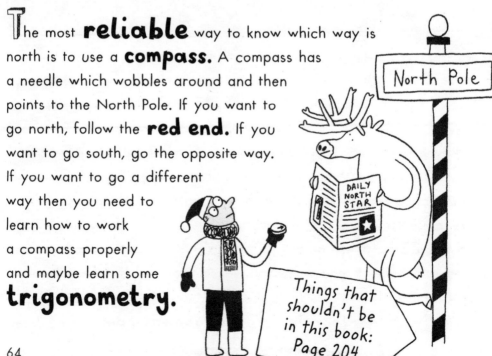

North Pole

DAILY NORTH STAR

Things that shouldn't be in this book: Page 204

If you don't have a compass, you can use the **sun.** First thing in the morning, the sun will rise in the **east.** At dusk, it will set in the **west.** However, it does tend to rise and set in a slightly different place each day. At midday, however, the sun should be to the **south** of you. So if it's sunny and you have a watch, it's possible to work out which way is which.

Another way to work out which way is north is to look at **lichen** growing on the side of a tree. Lichen prefers to grow on the **north** side of trees.

You can use all these **techniques** to navigate your way around a new school although if there are no trees inside your school you should look out for lichen on your **teacher's face.** According to the *SAS Survival Handbook* the noses of most **caretakers** usually face south.

School map: Page 12

Lollipop ladies

I have a part time job as a **lollipop lady.** I would have preferred to be a lollipop MAN but they only wanted lollipop ladies. I don't mind because it's the same outfit – just different **underwear.**

Lollipop ladies are disappearing. When I was at school there were millions but now they are an **endangered species.** According to my research there are more snow leopards in the Himalayas than there are lollipop ladies.

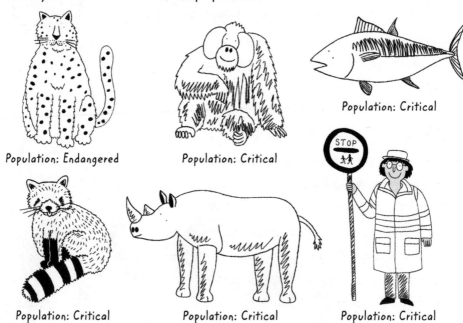

Population: Endangered   Population: Critical   Population: Critical

Population: Critical   Population: Critical   Population: Critical

The problem is that they are being **replaced** by pedestrian crossings, zebra crossings and speed bumps.

Going to school: Page 16

How teachers get to school: Page 24

According to *The Lollipop Legends* (which is a book I can't be bothered to write), when a lollipop lady dies, she is buried under a **speed bump.** That way she can still protect the children, even from beyond the grave. Legend also says that on a full moon, lollipop ladies rumble and stir. They rise again and walk the land like **luminous zombies.**

When I was little, we would occasionally see a **wild lollipop lady** in the woods. There are hardly any wild lollipop ladies left any more but you can help. In the autumn, rake up a pile of leaves behind a shed or against a wall. A wild lollipop lady can use this as a **nest** and it might just help them get through another winter.

Playground assistants

You'll find these **wonderful creatures** at primary schools, lurking around the playground at break time and lunchtime. They have been **specially made** in laboratories

to be able to watch hundreds of children all at the same time and check that no one is being too silly or dangerous. They are also trained in putting **ice packs** on the heads of children who have fallen over and hurt their knee.

Playground:
Page 58

Playground
games: Page 62

Excuses for being late for school

If you are little, it's **never** your fault for being late. Your grown-ups are in charge of that. But as you get bigger, you will start getting **responsibilities.** Responsibilities like emptying the dishwasher, feeding the dog and carrying granny up the stairs.

You might also have to **walk** to school on your own. This is great and means you can have all sorts of **adventures** looking at all the amazing stuff there is to see on the way. (Like pools of lava, bounty hunters and wandering snow leopards.)

You're doing a wonderful job, dear!

Being late: Page 84

But it also means that you are responsible for getting to school **on time.** And sometimes, you will get this wrong and be late. If you are anything like me, most of the time, you won't know why you were late. Sometimes I oversleep but many times I just **lose track** of what time it is, where I am and what it is I'm supposed to be doing. Here, however, are some excellent excuses for being late. Use them **wisely.**

There is one excuse that you can **famously** use only once a year. It's when the clocks go forward. Your excuse is:

Frogspawn story: Page 30

How teachers get to school: Page 24

Maths: Page 152

I'm sorry I'm late, Miss. I forgot to change the clocks.

I have, however, found a way to use this **excuse** at any time of year.

Teacher: Why are you late?

Child: I put the clocks back by mistake.

Teacher: But it's February. No one puts the clocks back in February.

Child: I know. I said it was a MISTAKE.

It's as simple as that.

Here are some more **excellent excuses:**

I'm sorry I'm late. I was carrying a goldfish bowl full of frogspawn.

The dog ate my alarm clock.

Going to school: Page 16

I rode my bike to school but I arrived to find that cats had stolen the bike racks and sold them for scrap metal. So I had to ride home and walk.

SWAG

Vikings invaded.

I forgot where the school was.

Quantum physics: Page 82

Quantum theory suggests the more I tried to analyse my lateness, the less I knew. I can only know where I am or how fast I'm going but not both at the same time. This makes it really difficult to navigate.

Slingshot effect

The slingshot effect (sometimes called 'Gravity Assist') is a way in which **astrophysicists** (the clever people who are in charge of astronauts) use the **gravity** of something in space (like the Moon) to increase the speed of their spaceships, biscuits or intergalactic **spaniels.**

FLOATING SPACE BISCUIT

SPACE DOG BISCUIT

Imagine a **spaceship** going around the Moon and imagine that the Moon is standing still. As the spaceship goes towards the Moon, it will be pulled in by the gravity of the Moon making it **travel faster.** As it goes around the other side of the Moon, it will keep the same speed and then when it leaves the Moon, it will slow down because the Moon's gravity will be trying to pull it back.

But – the Moon is NOT standing still. The Moon is travelling around the Earth **really fast.** It is travelling at about 6,500 kilometres per hour. And so, as the spaceship is travelling around the back of the Moon, the Moon drags the spaceship with it, which makes the spaceship go **even faster!**

The speed of the Moon also slows down ever so slightly but because the Moon is so big compared to the spaceship you can't really notice. What you do notice is that your spaceship goes **shooting off** much faster in whatever direction you have planned it to.

This is how you can use the slingshot effect to **accelerate** spaceships, biscuits and dogs to explore space faster.

What is also really **interesting** is that although this works on a space level it doesn't necessarily work on a teeny tiny quantum level. If you want to find out more about this ask a quantum physicist or a really **clever duck.**

That's PROFESSOR Clever Duck to you.

Science: Page 50

Quantum physics: Page 82

Dinner ladies

You might have looked at dinner ladies and school lunches and **wondered** these questions:

Who are dinner ladies?

Why is the food so terrible?

Why would the school employ people who can't cook when there are plenty of good cooks around?

Lunchtime: Page 52

Kitchen: Page 174

Dinner ladies are like secret, **undercover criminals.** They look like all they do is cook food, throw pans around and listen to the radio but really ...

They are actually in charge of the *whole* school.

None of the teachers actually want dinner ladies to cook the dinner. Some school dinners are the **worst** meals in the world. The dinner ladies, however, have all ganged up together and **forced** all the head teachers to employ them as dinner ladies. They are like a kind of **cabbagey mafia.**

Whatever you do, don't make them angry.

Things they don't teach you in school

Most teachers have a big list of things they are **supposed** to teach you. However, there is also a list of things that they are **not** supposed to teach you. These include: how to drive a lorry, how to have a conversation with a horse and how to train bees.

I am now very old. So old that I **make noises** I don't mean to. (I make noises when I sit down, get in the bath or bend over after eating beans.) Because I am so old I have learned many **wise** things that are not on the teachers' list of things to teach you.

One: Always Eat A Good Breakfast

If you get breakfast wrong, everything will fall apart. **Tiny green men** will invade your underpants drawer, an asteroid the size of Egypt will appear on a collision course to Earth and one of your neighbours' feet will fall off. All because you didn't eat your breakfast.

Two: Don't Argue With Anyone

How food affects your learning: Page 184

Ever. It's just not worth it. A much better plan is to pretend you agree with them, find out their address and post them an envelope of **glitter.**

Three: Don't Do Number Two If You Live In The Same House As The Person You Disagreed With

You will be asked to clean it up and it will take **100** years.

Four: Always Carry An Emergency Banana

Keep it in your packed lunch, your snack box or in your bag. It doesn't really matter where you keep it, just make sure you have an **emergency banana** at your disposal every day.

Emergencies you might need a banana for: Page 176

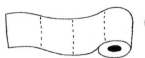 # Toilets

At some point in your school day, you are going to have to go to the **toilet.** And I'm afraid to say that school toilets are not the best.

For a start, the doors of the cubicles don't go all the way to the floor or the ceiling. This is so small children can't lock themselves in. But it also means that people can see your **poo face** as they walk past.

Greaseproof toilet paper

When I was at school, the other terrible thing was that the toilet roll was made out of some sort of scratchy **greaseproof paper.** If you weren't careful you could give yourself some serious **bum damage.**

When you're at school, your teacher may give you **learning objectives.** It might be to learn your nine times table or learn: to; use – punctuation' – properly

When I went to my son's first **parents' evening,** his teacher told us that his first learning objective for that term was to …

STOP PAINTING THE WALLS OF THE TOILET WITH WATER FROM THE TOILET!

This seemed like a reasonable request. He was in Reception then and now he is much older so he has learned to paint the walls of the toilet with **mayonnaise** instead.

How to fart without pooing yourself: Page 104

Sitting on your bottom: Page 128

MAYONNAISE FOR PAINTING

Boarding schools

For most children the **end** of the school day is something to look forward to. When that bell goes they can all run outside to see their grown-ups eagerly waiting to take them home.

Children who go to boarding school however, don't go home until the end of term! That can be as long as twelve weeks! **TWELVE WEEKS.**

Children go to **boarding schools** for lots of reasons. These include:

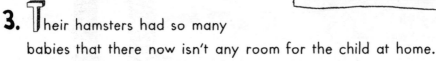

1. The school is a long way from home. Like in the remote mountains where the only company for miles around is goats.

2. Their grown-ups travel around as secret agent ninja spies and decide it would be better if the child were in one place.

3. Their hamsters had so many babies that there now isn't any room for the child at home.

Sharing a room with lots of other children must be a great way to make new friends. In fact, **boarding schools** are places famous for making friends who will be your friends for life! Or your **frenemies.**

What teachers do when you're not there: Page 192

The teachers at boarding schools tend to be very similar to normal teachers but some of them actually choose to **live** at the school. These teachers either have very **annoying families** of their own or are not safe to live in the real world for some reason.

I would live in the town but when there's a full moon I tend to get a little strange.

Quantum physics

Quantum physics is the **science** of really small things at a really tiny level.

What I find interesting is that really, really small things don't **behave** according to the same laws that normal-sized things do. For example, if I drop a ball on to a flat surface it will bounce back straight upwards.

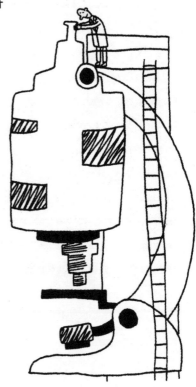

But if I drop a teeny tiny **photon** (the teeniest dot of light that you can imagine) on to a flat surface it might bounce straight up or it might fly off super fast in a completely random direction. In fact, at a **quantum level** you can work out how fast something is going and you can work out where it is BUT you can't know both things **at the same time.**

This makes working out a **quantum train timetable** almost impossible.

Time | Destination | Plat | Expt

$\langle \phi / \phi_m \rangle =$ London Paddington $\langle \phi_n / \int d\frac{2}{x}/x \rangle \langle x/\phi_x \rangle$

$\phi_n(x) = \langle x/\phi_n \rangle$ Didcot Parkway $-\frac{1}{2} \phi\hat{n}(x) = \phi_n/x\rangle$

$\langle \phi_n / \phi_n \rangle =$ Swansea $\int \hat{A}_x^{-1/2} /\phi_n'x \rangle / e \int d_x'^2 \frac{1}{x} = (\frac{1}{2} = 1$

$\langle \phi / \phi_o 1 \rangle =$ Bristol Temple Mds $\langle \phi_x / \int dx/x/\langle x/\phi m^2 \rangle$

$|\Psi(x)|\frac{2}{\pi}|\Psi_o|^2 e$

$\int_{-\infty}^{\infty} dx e^{-Ax^2} \frac{1}{\sqrt{\frac{\pi}{A}}}$

$\langle \langle y \times x_2 \rangle \rangle$

$= \langle \Psi_a^2 | (x - x_o)$

$\int dx / x \rangle \langle x = \mathbb{I} \rangle$

Departures

It also means that if you ever decide to have a **quantum barbecue** you'll never know when the sausages will be cooked.

It does mean, however, that if you are late for school, you can alway blame **quantum mechanics.**

Excuses for being late for school: Page 69

Science: Page 50

Being late

Being late is **terrible.** It feels like the whole world is turning inside out right in the middle of your tummy.

Teachers do not like it when you are late. They get really annoyed. If anyone was late when I was at school, my teacher would look really **disappointed** and then **sad.** Then steam would start to come out of her ears and she would start smelling like the inside of a fat labradoodle.

No one ever wanted that to happen so we did our best **not** to be late.

I think I smell lovely.

Emergencies you might need a banana for: Page 176

Excuses for being late for school: Page 69

The office: Page 138

84

I'm sorry I'm late, Miss. My mum has no sense of urgency.

Often, when you're late, it's not even your fault. It's your grown-up's fault because they are **responsible** for you.

If this is the case, it's okay to say so.

The best thing to do is **not** be late. If you can't be on time then be early. **Anyone** can be early.

The first time I took my little boy to school I was so **worried** about being late that we got there before the caretaker did. It was still dark.

Dad! It's Sunday!

If you can't be late, be early.

Allergy children

Some staffrooms have pictures of children on the walls with information about the **allergies** and **illnesses** they have. They look a bit like **wanted posters.**

Food allergies are, of course, **very serious.**
I am allergic to nuts and if I eat them I
get really poorly.
Sometimes people
offer me a bowl
of nuts and when I
say that I am allergic
they take the nuts
away and **hide** them.
I always find this funny
because I am *allergic* to
nuts. I am not *afraid*
of nuts.

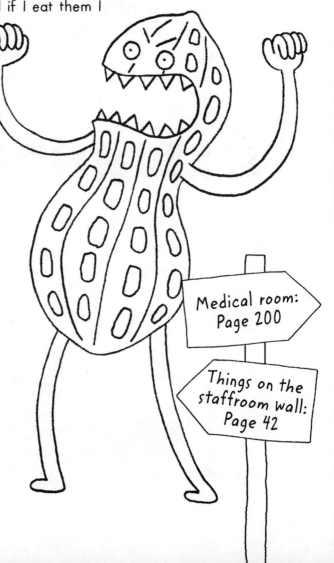

Medical room:
Page 200

Things on the
staffroom wall:
Page 42

Sports day

Have you ever watched the **Olympics** and thought, 'I wish I could I have a go at that'? Well, once a year, you can – at your school sports day! On this day you will have to do a variety of **weird tasks** involving beanbags, hoops, hockey sticks and jars of honey. There will often be a **running race.**

If you are really lucky, there will be a running race for teachers but in most schools this has been **banned** because they get far too **competitive.**

The best thing about sports days is that the sports you have to do always seem to be things that you've never done before – like **tossing beanbags** into a hoop. It's fun to spend all year playing football every lunchtime and then get tested on your ability to crawl through a **wobbly tunnel.**

Carpet area

Most classrooms have **one corner** that is carpeted. Teachers tend to use the carpet area for playing with toys at the weekend. And **itching their bottoms** like dogs.

Some of the less bonkers teachers use the carpet area for **story time,** which is the best part of school and makes all the boring stuff worthwhile.

Seeing your teacher in the real world: Page 124

What teachers do when you're not there: Page 192

Classrooms

Inventors have a laboratory.
The President of the USA has the Oval Office.
Editors have a lair.
Doctors have a surgery.
Teachers have a **classroom.**

It's where they spend most of their time. They put their name on the door, put up their favourite inspirational posters on the walls and sometimes grow unusual vegetables on the window sill.

The teachers' classroom is where you will spend most of your time at school. It's like your **base,** your living room and your bedroom all rolled into one. Although don't go to sleep in your classroom. They don't like it when you do that.

My favourite part of any classroom is the **magical corner** called the Carpet Area. You will often get asked to come and sit in this bit. It is a magical area where NO SHOES ARE ALLOWED.

Something very important that you might see on the wall of your classroom is some kind of **chart** or system for getting you to behave yourself. It might be house points or it might be **walking the plank.**

At most **primary schools,** you'll spend most of your time in the one classroom but as you get older you might find yourself having to go to different rooms for different sorts of lessons. There might be an art room or a science lab or a **farting library.**
Whatever you do, don't go to the farting library immediately after the Reception children have had lunch. It's the worst thing ever.

Class names:
Page 92

Carpet area:
Page 89

How teachers motivate you:
Page 94

Primary schools:
Page 48

91

Class names

One of the first things that happens when you start school is that you get put in a particular class. That class will have a teacher in charge of it and might also have a **name.**

Sometimes the classes just have a number or a letter. You might find yourself in **Class 4B.** Often your class will have the same name as a pencil.

Other times, classes are named after colours or trees or cute fluffy animals. You might discover that your class is called Blue or Oak or that you have become one of the **Hedgehogs.**

There must be some things that classes are NEVER named after though. Types of **power tools**, different **forks** and your granny's **cats** spring to mind.

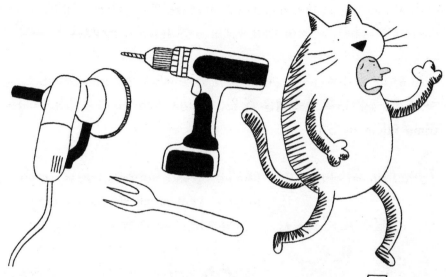

Something has gone **very wrong** if you turn up at school to find that you are going to be in the Fish Fork Class, you'll be spending the year in Mr Fluffy-wuffkins or you'll be doing your learning in the Dewalt Brushless 18v Lithium-ion Keyless Cordless Drill Driver Room.

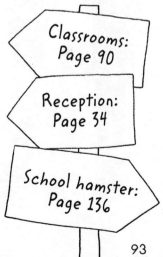

Classrooms: Page 90

Reception: Page 34

School hamster: Page 136

How teachers motivate you

Some teachers like to find ways to make you **work harder** and stop you from being naughty. On the wall next to their desk you will probably find some sort of chart. Sometimes it involves **house points.** Occasionally it involves **Olympic medals.** Often it involves colours.

There will probably be **little pictures** of everyone's faces. These are used as counters to show how everyone is doing.

It might be that at the start of the day everyone is in green. If you do something bad, you go down to orange or even red and if you do something good, you go up to blue or golden or a **shiny-angel-face.**

It's very important to do your best to be in the good part of this sort of thing. You might get it **wrong** sometimes though. And if you do, you might get **punished** ... When I was at primary school I only got into trouble **twice.**

The first was for writing a play in maths class. (I had finished my maths so I thought I would just get on with the play I was writing. Apparently, I should have asked for **more maths.** Who asks for more maths?!)

The second time was for writing a poem, which simply listed the number of **lamp posts** in each street around our school. It was a **protest** against not being allowed to write poetry that rhymed and I was really **proud** of it.

House points: Page 28

My scale of teacher behaviour: Page 98

Classrooms: Page 90

Punishments: Page 120

Forest schools

Lots of teachers now choose to have some of their lessons in a forest school. These teachers often wear **waterproof trousers** all the time and can do impressions of songbirds. They live in bushes and have lots of **friends** who are all deer. So what is a forest school?

A forest school is a **brilliant idea** for getting children out of the classroom and doing their learning amongst the trees instead. Teachers might do the same lesson as normal except you're all **outside** or they might use what's around them to **inspire** your learning. Some forest schools simply do everything outside – even if the weather is bad. Children just **wrap up** nice and warm and potter about learning about acorns and squirrels, leaves and mud and the wonderful wisdom of trees.

Different types of teacher and where to find them: Page 14

Things that shouldn't be in this book: Page 204

I am a big fan of forest schools, although if you end up in one watch out for **bear attacks** and **Robin Hood.** Bears are really dangerous and Robin Hood is really annoying because he is always singing songs. It's fun for a while but after the seventh time of singing *Here We Go Round the Mulberry Bush* you will want to stuff your ears with leaves and hide behind a rock.

La la laaaaaa!!

If you get **chased** by a bear whilst at forest school, or anywhere else, just run down hill and then stop really quickly. Bears have really **heavy bums** and if they do an emergency stop, their bums send them rolling over themselves and down the hill.

If someone uphill from you is being chased by a bear, be careful not to get **run over** by the bear.

My scale of teacher behaviour

Teachers may have behaviour charts and house points and stars but who's judging **them?** I have my **own scale** for judging the behaviour or teachers ...

If you start in the middle you will see that it says **Nice.** Nice is easy to achieve. A teacher's default setting is Nice.

Nice

Default mode

They can, of course, attempt to get promoted to the next level up which is **Good.** Good requires a bit of effort. Good teachers have to take time to help every child and remember who they all are. They also have to not get **cross** when they're teaching things that no one understands like relative clauses.

Good

Or teachers can go the other direction to **Naughty.** Naughty teachers do things like send you out to play when it's **raining** and make you sit in a boy-girl-boy pattern in assemblies.

Naughty

Bad

The next level down from Naughty is **BAD.** Bad teachers don't turn up on time in the morning, forget what they're supposed to be teaching and smell of petrol for some reason.

Handwriting:
Page 180

How teachers
motivate you:
Page 94

At the very top of the scale is **Angel.** Angel teachers are the best in the world. They probably spend their own money buying books for the school and they will teach you so well that they will literally change your whole life.

Angel

And then of course, at the very bottom of the scale of teacher behaviour is ... **Evil!**

Evil

You can spot them by the way their eyes glow in the dark and fire comes out of their fingertips. Their purpose in life is to open a portal to the netherworld to release demons, basilisks and supply teachers. If you find yourself being taught by one of these **evil teachers,** ask to be moved to another school immediately or at least make sure you've got some **garlic** in your packed lunch.

Assembly hall

Somewhere in your school, usually in the middle you will find a huge room called an **Assembly Hall.** Sometimes there is more than one. There might be a lower and an upper hall. Or a large hall and a small hall. It's a bit like how your body has a large intestine and a small intestine. Lots of school halls actually smell like **intestines** too.

Most of the time, though, the hall will just be called **The Hall.** The Hall is usually **freezing cold.**

People's voices sound different in there. Some have a piano in the corner, others have a stage. Some have a picture of the very first head teacher to tell someone off. He glares down at the room to remind you to **behave yourself.**

I see everything.

School dinners: Page 122

Tests and exams: Page 108

Assemblies: Page 106

P.E.: Page 188

How to fart without pooing yourself

When you were a baby you wore **nappies.** This was great because you could do a wee or a poo whenever you wanted to. It also meant that if you did a **bottom burp** but then discovered that it was actually more serious, you could do an unintended poo and everything would be fine.

Once you were potty trained, however, this situation changed. Now, you have a problem. When you feel like you need to fart you have to do so without **accidentally** pooing yourself.

Sometimes I have trouble with this myself but generally speaking I have solved the problem by being **very careful** about my farts. I used to spend a lot of time doing yoga and meditating and through this practice I learned to hold in farts until the end of the yoga class or sometimes release them slowly in a kind of **staggered** release so that they didn't make any noise.

This also means that you have **more time** to work out whether this really is just a fart or if you are going to need to get out of your leotard really quickly.

Keep practising and be aware of your **own bum.** This isn't something they teach you in school but believe you me, your teacher is doing the **exact same thing.**

If you are under the age of eight it's also a good idea to only fart if you are near a toilet. And don't fart in a lift or next to a barbecue. **Ever!**

Toilets:
Page 78

FINANCIAL TIMES

Assemblies

Assembly Hall:
Page 102

People who are in the army often get captured in the middle of a battle. They are sent to a **prison** where they have to stay until the war is over. Once a day, the guards will ring a bell and everyone will have to assemble in the central square so they can count all the prisoners and make sure someone hasn't **escaped** during the night. A similar thing happens in **primary schools.**

Once a week or so, everyone in the school has to go into the hall so they can sing songs, be presented with certificates and counted to check that no one has dug a tunnel under the library and is halfway to **Switzerland.**

Teachers are usually **in charge** of assemblies and they like to do all sorts of things when it's their turn. Sometimes they tell a story and sometimes they tell everyone off at the same time if everyone has been doing something wrong. Examples include:

> Everyone needs to stop going on the field when it is muddy because it is ruining the grass.

> Everyone needs to stop doing massive poos because they are blocking up the plumbing system.

> Everyone needs to do less maths as we have run out of numbers.

Sometimes in assembly, everyone gets **told off** for something that only one person has done.

> We are not going to leave this hall until I find out who has taken all the felt!

Attack of the wasp: Page 150

Tests and exams

If you are cooking sausages you don't just leave them on for twenty minutes and then eat them. You have to **test** to see if they have been cooked properly. There are many ways to test how well a sausage has been cooked. The first is to see what **colour** it is. Pink is not cooked, brown is cooked. Black is extremely cooked and you probably shouldn't eat it.

You can also test a sausage by poking it with a fork to see what the juices are like inside and if you **really** want to be sure that it is cooked all the way through, you have to **CHOP IT IN HALF.**

The problem with **chopping** it in half is that it really messes up the **sausage!**

Every now and again, your teachers will need to test to see how much you have **learned.**

Some children get really **stressed** about this. But there really isn't anything to worry about. Your test results won't have any effect on what happens to you at school or in the **real world.**

THEY ARE NOT TESTING YOU.

They are testing your teachers to see how well you've been **taught.** It's a bit like when the garage tests your car to see if it's safe to drive.

A similar sort of thing happens when the school gets **inspected** ... The teachers get so scared that often a little bit of wee comes out but **you** have literally nothing to worry about.

Assembly hall: Page 102

Inspections: Page 130

School plays

Often at Christmas, and sometimes at the end of the summer term, one of your teachers might decide they would like to organise a **play.** These are a great way to find out what you're made of and stretch what you thought was possible.

And you get to wear a **costume.** What's not to like?

When I was seven, I once played the part of **Santa Claus** and because I was unable to grow a beard for the part, they made one by sticking cotton wool to my face with gloopy PVA glue. It took until Easter before it all came off.

STOP

Pasta Picasso: Page 118

Art: Page 172

During the production of every school play the following things are **guaranteed** to happen:

Someone will be poorly and have to be replaced with someone who doesn't know the words.

Someone will forget their words and a teacher will have to shout the words to them.

The teacher organising the play will have a meltdown and have to go lie down for a while.

A piece of scenery will fall over.

Someone will be sick.

The school hamster will escape and terrorise the audience.

Teacher profiles

There are lots of different **types** of teachers – just like there are lots of different breeds of **dogs** and **cats**. Here are a few of my favourite.

LOVELY

Everyone wants to get the **lovely teacher.** She usually has a symmetrical face, wears really soft cardigans and will always have an apple on her desk. They are often called things like:

Miss Honey
Mrs Donaghy
Mr Sausage

This teacher is probably everyone's **favourite.**

OLD

There is always one teacher who is **so old** he gets lost in the wrong corridor and has to be gently guided back to his classroom or to the medical room for a nap.

He still talks about **measuring** things in ounces and inches and can remember buying things in shillings.

Teachers through time: Page 36

Pre-decimalisation maths: Page 140

Different types of teacher and where to find them: Page 14

P.E. TEACHER

He usually has **an injury** of some sort and a support bandage, can be seen holding a sports drink and often **smells** of Deep Heat. He is always asking you if you saw the game last night. You reply, 'No I didn't. The game doesn't start until after my bedtime.'

My P.E. teacher always wore his sports kit but I never saw him do any **actual** sports. Mostly he just stood around shouting at us to do things.

Other teachers might tell you that P.E. teachers aren't **clever** enough to be proper teachers but I think that getting yourself a job where all you do is get kids to run around is actually very clever indeed.

SMELLY

This is the teacher who smells of coffee and stinky perfume. You will maybe notice lots of breath mints in their pocket but it definitely isn't helping!

There is no way to put this nicely. Some teachers just smell really **bad.** Some of them smell of wet dogs. Some smell of manky flowers. Others smell of **goldfish.**

How teachers get to school:
Page 24

Seeing your teacher in the real world:
Page 124

SUPPLY

There are many types of supply teacher. It is important that you recognise which type you've got as quickly as possible so you can **adapt** your learning behaviour accordingly.

Here is an example of the Newly Qualified Supply Teacher. Note the **sweat patches** and the **worried** look on his face. He will spook easily.

SUPER COOL

This guy is some sort of **hipster.** He wears black, has tattoos and travelled extensively before becoming a teacher.

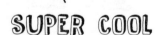

Head teachers: Page 144

Accidentally calling your teacher mum: Page 149

Sitting on your bottom: Page 128

HUGE

This is a **semi-giant** teacher who booms down at you from a great height. He has clouds floating around his head and a fiercely large bottom that entirely engulfs a piano stool.

Pasta Picasso

Once in a primary school I saw a picture of Picasso's *Guernica*, made entirely with different types of **pasta** glued on to a piece of **sugar paper.** I've also seen projects where some teacher thought it would be a great idea to recreate Matisse's *Snail* made from bits of paper and Degas' *Ballet Dancers* created by sticking individual grains of rice together.

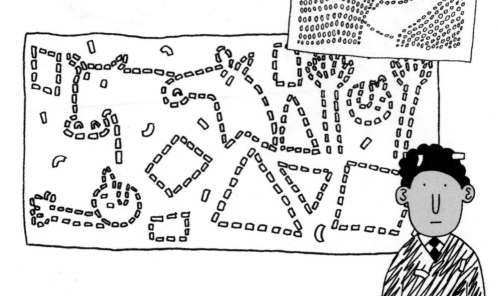

Art teachers can be blamed for a lot of bad recreations of work. **ESPECIALLY PASTA ART.**

The Pasta Picasso effect didn't really work. This was probably because **Picasso** is one of the greatest artists ever and the child that made the pasta picture was six and had only recently learned how to fart without **pooing himself.** And also because the child had stuck most of the pasta to himself and eaten the rest.

STOP

Tissue paper Monet: Page 148

Art: Page 172

How to fart without pooing yourself: Page 104

Punishments

Teachers see everything. They are **eagle-eyed** and can sense misbehaving from miles off. If you do the wrong thing at school you might find yourself being **punished** by your teacher.

Wrong things might include:

1. Being **late** all the time.

2. Not **bothering** to do your homework.

3. Talking when you're supposed to be working.

4. Covering yourself with glue and rolling in a giant pile of **glitter** whilst singing, 'Look at me, I'm a disco worm!'

Woooo!

Punishments might include:

1. **N**ot being allowed out to **play** and having to do work instead.

2. **B**eing moved to a different table.

3. **B**eing told to **write lines** out again and again.

4. **B**eing sent away to sea and then tied to a mast while a large man with gold, hoopy earrings sings the songs from all the adverts that you don't like.

How teachers motivate you: Page 94

Teachers through time: Page 36

Chunky chicken chops are chewy and cheesy.

121

School dinners

Whenever I go to a school I always have a school lunch. Sometimes they are **delicious** and sometimes they nearly kill me. Sometimes you get a full roast dinner and sometimes you get a weird wrinkly sausage that looks like it's crawled out of a **dead elephant.**

When I pick up my son from school on **Thursdays,** I always ask him what he had for lunch. He always says,

We had fishy chicken again.

Apparently, **fishy chicken** is chicken that tastes like fish. I've suggested to him that it might just be fish but he says it definitely says chicken on the menu and the **dinner ladies** have promised him that it is chicken. It's just that it looks and tastes like fish.

The problem at his school is that the dinner ladies don't actually cook the food at the school. It is cooked by dandruff-ridden **trolls** in a cave over a hundred miles a way. It is then packed into bags made from the **bladders** of buffalo, chucked on to the back of a **camel** and yomped around the county to loads of different schools. The food started off being reasonably tasty but by the time it gets to the children, it has gone cold, **soggy** and the chicken looks and tastes like **fish.**

Kitchen: Page 174

How food affects your learning: Page 184

123

Seeing your teacher in the real world

This is one of the **weirdest** things that will happen to you and your teacher. You're in the supermarket, doing your shopping when you see your teacher, pushing a trolley ... wearing jeans ... with her husband ... and her own children.

What weirdness is this?

The thing to do is stand perfectly still until the situation stops. Or dive into a freezer and **hide** under the bags of peas.

Another place you might see your teacher is **on holiday.** If this happens, the best thing for everyone is just to pretend that it isn't happening. Then, when you are next at school and you are asked to write a **story** about what you did at the holidays, you can say:

> I went to the beach and saw Mr Wilbraham wearing tiny swimming shorts.

The only thing I can think of that might be even **more weird** than this would be if your parents are friends with your teacher and your teacher comes over for dinner ... to your house. That should be **illegal** as it damages children, teachers and the fabric of the universe.

Does your grown-up really like your teacher?: Page 142

125

Nursery

Before you are old enough to go to **proper school,** you might find yourself at nursery, pre-prep or kindergarten. This isn't really school at all and is more like rolling around in sand, picking each other's noses.

Sometimes I visit nursery schools to tell them **stories.** I'm never really sure whether they are listening or not and I always come out the other side with something **sticky** on my shirt.

Forest schools:
Page 96

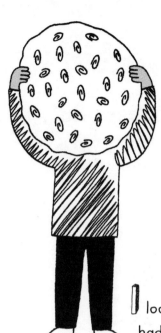

Often, they give me **presents** at the end. One day, a little boy gave me a cardboard moon that he had made. It was round, and he had painted it with silvery paint. And so I asked him ...

> What is this?

> It's a moon.

I looked more closely and saw that he had also glued about twenty-seven **paper clips** on to his moon.

> I love this, but what are these things?

> That's the 'clips of the moon.

> Oh. The eclipse.

This reminds me that you should **never** judge a book by its cover and just because a child is no taller than your knee and is covered in someone else's breakfast, doesn't mean that they aren't very, very **clever** inside their brain and heart.

127

Sitting on your bottom

In many schools up until the age of ten or so, you will often be told by a teacher to sit on your **bottom.**

When I was at school I was always being told to sit on my bottom because I used to **fidget.** I didn't learn how to sit still until I was about thirty-four and up until then my teacher would yell ...

> James! Sit on your bottom!

If you think about it, you can't really sit on anything else. You can sit on a chair. You can sit on a carpet. You can sit on a **rainbow unicorn** if you like but you are still sitting on your bottom. You need your bottom to do the sitting with.

Once, when I was at school I was told to sit on my bottom for the **millionth time** and I thought to myself, *Maybe she means, sit on YOUR bottom.*

So I tried sitting on **someone else's** bottom.

Then I really got into **trouble.**

JAMES!

Carpet area:
Page 89

Inspections

If you go to an **animal rescue** shelter and ask if you can have one of their dogs, they will come to your house and check that your home is **suitable** for a dog: that there is enough space, you have a garden that the dog can run around in and won't **escape** from, you don't own forty-three other dogs already and someone is willing to clear up the poo.

This is called an **inspection.**

Tests and exams: Page 108

A similar thing happens in **schools.**

Every couple of years someone will come to your school to **check** that the teachers are teaching you the right things. They will also make sure that you have plenty of room to **run around** in, you can't **escape** from the playground, there aren't forty-three other children in your class and someone is willing to clear up all the **poo.**

When an inspection happens, your teacher gets a couple of days notice. You will find that they get really **stressed.** Just let them get on with it. You might get asked to behave better and not to **wee** on the ceiling but just remember: the inspectors are inspecting the teachers, **not you.** They are on your side.

What on Earth are libraries?

Sometimes, your teacher might suggest that you join the local **library.** So what is a library?

Most towns and some villages have one. They have existed for thousands of years as a place to keep books and store **knowledge.** Being in a room that is full of books is a marvellous thing. Just think about how many words there are in a library. Each of those words has been thought of and carefully chosen by tens of thousands of people. That must make it a **special place** to be.

All sorts of things happen in libraries and are improved by being surrounded by **books.** I take my daughter to a tiny tots sing-along. Twenty babies roll around singing *The Wheels on the Bus* for half an hour or until someone is **sick** (sometimes that someone is me).

Occasionally, you see that a library is being used for **puppet shows** or cheese-tasting

The school library: Page 154

events. Sometimes, they have **authors** visiting and talking about their books or **storytellers** telling their tales. All of these activities are much better because they are in a library. I wonder if **scooter racing** would be better there.

Who has taken all the felt?: Page 44

Going to school: Page 16

Felt making would definitely be better in a library. As would flower-arranging, fish and chips and **paper aeroplane competitions.**

Catapulting to school

I have invented a **new way** to get children to school. It doesn't involve having to struggle through any traffic and you don't need any petrol to get there.

It is a giant catapult!

All you would have to do is sit yourself in the catapult, then one of your grown-ups would wind up the mechanism and **BOIIING!** You would be catapulted through the air, over the houses, across the town, all the way to school.

Obviously, to be safe, there would need to be a **massive trampoline** in the playground to land on. It would be so much fun in the mornings if everyone came bouncing in from all over the place.

I'm not sure how you'd get home though. You couldn't have a catapult for everyone at school. There wouldn't be **enough room.** Maybe you could have one catapult that the caretaker is in charge of. At the end of the day, everyone would queue up to be catapulted home.

And you'd have to make sure you got catapulted to the **right house.**

Going to school: Page 16

School hamster

Hamsters are very **popular** pets. If you are very lucky your teacher will introduce one as a classroom pet that will live in the corner of the room in a cage.

Children can get it out and make it **climb up** their jumper sleeve and nest in their armpits until they realise that this is the most **ticklish** thing in the world and they are giggling so much that a little bit of wee has come out of the child. And the hamster.

Hi!

The **other thing** that happens with the school hamster is that during the holidays, someone gets to take the school hamster home with them and look after it until school starts again. This is very **exciting** for the child who has been chosen as ...

THE GUARDIAN OF THE HAMSTER

The Guardians of the Hamster go back thousands of years. The first ones looked after school hamsters during the time of the **Egyptian Pharaohs.** I say 'looked after' but what they really did was wrap them in bandages and turn them into tiny **mummies.** Since then, they have handed down the **responsibility** of looking after hamsters from one generation to the next.

If you get asked to be a Guardian of the Hamster, you must take the responsibility very **seriously** and look after the hamster as best you can. Love it. Feed it. Protect it from **cats.** And whatever you do, **don't sit on it.**

Excuse me! I think you'll find your bum is on me.

137

The office

There is usually only one way in or out of a school and that is the **main entrance.** This is like the main gate of a castle. Castles had huge metal portcullis gates, a drawbridge and a couple of blokes sitting on the top with pots of boiling oil, ready to pour on their **enemies.** Schools used to have this too until health and safety said they had to get rid of it.

The receptionist is the **magical guardian** of the whole school. She will only let you into the rest of the school if you sign in a book, wear a badge and answer a riddle.

The school secretary: Page 146

Head teachers: Page 144

I have feathers but I swim. I am not a penguin. What am I?

Fishy chicken?

Behind reception is usually where the head teacher lives. You will meet your **head teacher** fairly quickly after your start in a school.

Most of the time, of course, you won't come into the school through **reception.** You will go in through your classroom's special door. If you are late though, you have to go through reception and tell them you are **late.**

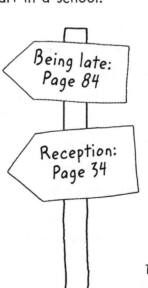

Being late: Page 84

Reception: Page 34

139

Pre-decimalisation maths

Ask your grandparents and they will confirm that **before 1971** maths was the most complicated subject ever. All the units for doing maths with were completely different from now and **crazy!**

Today, if you're learning how to do maths you know that there are **100 pence** in 1 pound, **1,000 grams** in 1 kilogram, **100 centimetres** in 1 metre and **1,000** metres in 1 kilometre. Right? You might need a lie down if maths isn't your strong point.

Before 1971, you had to remember that there were **20 shillings** in 1 pound of money but **16 ounces** in 1 pound of weight.

There were also **14 pounds** of weight in 1 stone, **12 inches** in 1 foot, **3 feet** in 1 yard and **1,760 yards** in 1 mile.

I'm exhausted just thinking about it! This made even the simplest of sums almost **impossible.** It took most children until they were fourteen to learn what all the units were — let alone do any **actual maths** with them.

Here are some **hilarious** examples of maths questions from the olden days. See if you can work out the answers. **Good luck!**

Question One: A train is travelling at seven yards per second. Another train is travelling towards this train at fourteen ounces per day. At what point will anyone care?

Answer One: Never.

Question Two: Timothy has fifty-seven pounds of sugar. He eats one hundred ounces of the sugar. What does he have now?

Answer Two: A stomach ache and three rotten teeth.

Question Three: A tractor and a plough costs fourteen guineas and uses four shillings of diesel a day to run. A carthorse and a plough costs seven pounds and eight shillings and costs half a sixpence a day to feed. If Farmer Giles buys both the tractor and the carthorse, how long will it take him to find an easier way to farm without unnecessarily turning the soil upside down twice a year?

Answer Three: When enough people tell him.

Does your grown-up really like your teacher?

You might think that teachers and your grown-ups are on the same side. They are all **adults,** aren't they? This might be the case but more often than not your grown-ups will have their own **relationship** with your teachers based on how happy they were at school when they were children.

If your dad, for example, really enjoyed school, was the captain of everything and had more badges on his blazer than a girl scout, then he will probably be really **enthusiastic** about your homework and encourage you to be like him.

But maybe your mum didn't enjoy school at all. Maybe she hated her teachers and was always getting **punished** for not being clever in the right way. If this is the case then your mum probably won't like your teacher either, even though your teacher probably hadn't even been born when your mum was at school.

<G>rown-ups are **strange creatures** at the best of times. I try to avoid them.

Accidentally calling your teacher mum: Page 149

143

Head teachers

The head teacher is in charge of the school and everything that happens in it. These **unusual creatures** are usually people who used to be teachers but they were so good at being teachers that they were given a job in which they don't get time to do any teaching any more.

I have met lots of head teachers and generally speaking, they fall into one of **three categories.**

1. Business-like

The business-like head teachers run their school like it's a **factory.** Everything happens for a reason and they get really excited about things like paperwork and reports. They like to tell you about their attendance figures and how much the new roof cost.

The office:
Page 138

144

2. Show-business-like

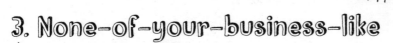

The show-business-like head teachers run their school like it's a **TV programme.** They wear really bright outfits and they are epically good at showing off during assemblies. They get the whole school excited about learning and doing stuff and everything is positive.

3. None-of-your-business-like

No one has any idea how the none-of-your-business-like head teachers run their school because they are always **busy** and you never get to meet to them. They are always in a meeting or away on a course. Often the only time they leave their office is when they are sitting in their car, eating **doughnuts** and playing games on their phone.

PIE PAD

The school secretary

If a school is like the **human body** then I suppose teachers are like the muscles. The head teacher is the heart. The classrooms are the bones and the corridors are the **nervous system.**

The brain of the school, however, is the **school secretary.** She is not a teacher. She doesn't mix with teachers. She takes her breaks at different times. Like a brain, she does all the thinking for the school.

The school secretary lives in the **office** near the main entrance of the school. If you are late, she is the person you have to tell. If your grown-up is going to pick you up in the middle of the afternoon to take you to the dentist, she is the person who needs to know. Also, if you need to know pretty much anything, the school secretary is the one to ask. They know **EVERYTHING.**

If you have lost something, she will either know where it is or have it in her **drawer.** If you don't know where you're supposed to be she will know and will put you there.

If you don't know which thing to wear, which after school club you're signed up for, where the toilet is or what on earth is going on with everything, ask the **school secretary.**

They also know when the next lunar eclipse will be,

how to grow an ash tree from seed, how to put on a pair of tights without using your hands and can tell which way is north with their **eyes closed.**

How to tell which way is north: Page 64

The office: Page 138

Tissue paper Monet

At some point a teacher will tell you to make a picture of Monet's *Water Lilies*, not with water colour paints but with scrunched up pieces of **tissue paper** stuck to the wall.

Like all good **impressionism**, the effect is best observed from far away — like from the other end of the hall, through your fingers.

If you want to know more about this **school of art** follow this signpost:

Pasta Picasso:
Page 118

Disappointillism:
Page 162

Accidentally calling your teacher mum

Literally the **worst thing** that can happen to you at school is when you accidentally call your teacher **'mum'**.

There is no way around this, you will go bright red, wish that the world would swallow you up and just sit feeling about how **awful** it is.

It'll be all right.

In a few weeks.

Attack of the wasp

My **favourite thing** that ever happened when I was in primary school took place one morning in the summer of my last year. We were having an assembly. I was sitting at the back with the other oldest children. The recorder teacher was making his group of **tuneless** pupils play a terrible version of a hymn called *All Things Bright and Beautiful.* (Look for it on YouTube – it's awesome!)

We were all singing this **beautifully** when a wasp flew through the window and started circling around the heads of the smallest children at the front.

One wasp can cause a lot of **trouble** in a school assembly. No one likes wasps. If wasps were an endangered species, would anyone care?

All things bright and beautiful,
All creatures great and small,
All things wise and wonderful,
The Lord God made them all.

Recorders: Page 54

Ohe of the smallest children noticed the **wasp** and pointed at it, probably saying, 'Ooh look. There is a wasp.' This information started **spreading** through the school as children either saw the wasp themselves or heard about it from another child.

Nursery: Page 126

Then the teachers noticed the wasp and one of them got a newspaper, rolled it up and started chasing after the wasp, trying to hit it with his **newspaper truncheon.** In order to do this, he had to wade into the mass of cross-legged kids who were terrified — not so much of the wasp but of being trod on by this **massive** teacher.

And so, half of the school were running away from a wasp in **terror.** And the other half of the school were still singing,

> All things bright and beautiful,
> All creatures great and small ...

Apparently this is called **irony** and I love it!

Assemblies: Page 106

Maths

Ah, the glories of **mathematics.** My favourite thing in maths when I was in school was imaginary numbers. Now this is **A Level** stuff so if you're eight years old you're going to have to concentrate really hard. Ready – here we go.

The square root of a number is the number that you would have to **multiply** BY ITSELF to get the first number.

So the square root of 9 is 3, because 3 x 3 = 9

If you multiply a negative number by a negative number you get a **positive number.**

So -2 x -2 = 4

If you multiply a negative number by a positive number you get a **negative number.**

So -4 x 6 = -24

So what's the **square root** of a minus number? How do you find a number that when you multiply it by itself makes a **minus number?**

What's the square root of -1?

It's not 1 because 1 x 1 = 1.

It's not -1 because -1 x -1 = 1.

It turns out that the answer is 'i'.

Not a number at all but a letter!

This was the point when I started to get really **angry** with maths. How can the square root of a number be a **letter?** That's like saying that the best type of bicycle in the world is soup.

Apparently, 'i' is something called an imaginary number. So not a real number, just an **imaginary** one. As far as I can tell, the only point of imaginary numbers is that you can use them as an **excuse** for being late for school.

> I set my alarm clock in imaginary numbers so I didn't wake up until the square root of minus seven o'clock.

Imaginary numbers are also really **useful** for working out how many places you need to set at the dinner table when you've invited all your imaginary friends round for tea.

Excuses for being late for school: Page 69

The school library

All schools should have a **library.** In some schools, it's the centre of the school and it feels like it's the heart of everything that is going on. In other schools, it's just a couple of shelves in a corridor or a place to keep books that no one reads.

If you're really **lucky,** your school will have a great **librarian** who is brilliant at helping you choose which book to read next. Your class will have regular lessons in the school library and you will be able to borrow books and take them home and read them.

The school library is also usually a **safe** and **warm** place to hang out. If you're lucky you might be allowed to be a librarian yourself and help look after the books.

If your school doesn't have a library or it needs some **improvement,** then why not join the school council and see if you can get things changed?

Or you could start your own library. All you need is a couple of thousand books. **Easy peasy.**

The librarian:
Page 160

School council:
Page 56

What on Earth are libraries?:
Page 132

Things that you only see in schools

Over the last twenty-three years I have visited over two and half thousand **schools.** Before that, of course, I was at school. So between my work and childhood, I have spent about thirty-five years in schools. Unlike teachers, however, I also spend time in the **real world.** Here are some things that you see all the time in primary schools but you never see in the real world.

Felt

What is felt? And why is it called 'felt'? You wouldn't make a material called 'heard', would you?

Who has taken all the felt?: Page 44

I love felt.

Recorders

These strange plastic instruments of **musical torture** are abundant in schools all around the world. I did a survey of 200 children and 97% of them had played the recorder at some point. The other 3% couldn't hear the question because of all the recorders.

I then did a **survey** of 200 teachers. 97% had taught children how to play the recorder at some point but only 43% of them could play the recorder themselves. This might be part of the problem.

Recorders: Page 54

Pencils

They say that if something isn't broken you shouldn't fix it. Pencils have been the same **forever!** Usually they are yellow and black striped. Sometimes they are red and white. But basically they are the same as they were when your **grandparents** were at school. When you leave school, however, you'll notice that no one uses pencils any more!

I don't think that's how you use a pencil, gran.

Primary schools: Page 48

Things that were normal for your parents: Page 196

Sitting on your bottom

In 1948, it was decided that children under the age of eleven didn't need chairs as they were too **expensive** and it was perfectly possible for a child to sit on its own bottom. This is still happening today, even though teachers never tell each other to sit on their bottoms.

STOP

Sitting on your bottom: Page 128

What teachers do when you're not there: Page 192

The librarian

School librarians are an **interesting species.** They are in the school but they are not necessarily part of the school. They are **not** teachers but you have to treat them like teachers.

They are usually hiding a terrible and **dark secret.** And it's your job to try and find out what that secret is.

Some librarians go home at the end of the day to normal houses. Most of them, however, live in **strange nests** that they have made between bookshelves. The nests are made from the shredded pages of books that have been banned by the head teacher.

The librarian has two main jobs in a school. The first is to be a little bit **different** from everyone else. Teachers tend to see things a certain way. It is the librarian's job to see things in a *different* way. Teachers are encouraged to see children as things to put knowledge in. Librarians tend to see children as things that need **connecting** up together with the world through books.

Their second job is to **recommend** books that you wouldn't necessarily think of reading. Go up to a librarian and say:

I've been reading this book about teachers and schools by James Campbell. What do you think I should read next?

The school library: Page 154

Disappointillism

Over the years, **artists** have often found themselves as part of schools of thought around art. They all have names like Pre-Raphaelites, Impressionists or Expressionists.

The **Disappointillists** were a group of artists who painted in the twentieth century. They created paintings that looked really **amazing** from a distance but as you went closer to look properly you would realise that they were actually utterly **terrible.**

Art:
Page 172

This form of art was extremely **unsuccessful** but it managed to cause ripples that are still having an effect today. How often have you seen something on the other side of the room and thought, 'ooh, that's looks interesting,' so you go over to look at it and realise that it's just **rubbish?** That's Disappointillism, that is.

FINANCIAL TIMES

I love Disappointillism so much that I've written a **poem** about it.

We are the Disappointillists,
Disasters one and all.
You've never seen such rubbish as
What we'll put on the wall.
We look like we are artists
But really we're less **smarty.**
Our paintings look quite hopeful
But actually they're just farty.
That's Disappointillism — that is.

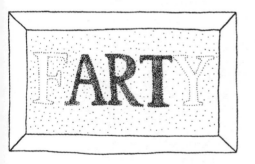

You see a picture on the wall,
The best — a **magnum opus.**
But when you see the thing up close
You realise that it's **bogus.**
Your distant first impression was
The brushwork was quite stunning.
But now the thing is in your face
The colours look like running.
That's Disappointillism — that is.

You hear a song on the **radio,**
And think, 'Yeah, that's my jam.'
But as you listen further
You realise it's just **spam.**

The first verse sounded
promising,
The groove makes you
light-headed.
But then the chorus whines
just like
A hamster being
shredded.
That's Disappointillism — that is.

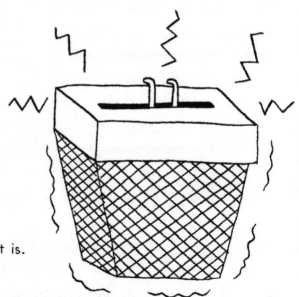

Your dad cooks up a tasty pie
It smells and looks quite yum.
But when you put it in your mouth
It tastes like **manky bum.**
By looking at its golden crust
Your gut says let's get to it.
But once that pie is in your mouth
You simply want to **spew** it.
That's Disappoinitillism – that is.

You start to read a poem,
The beginning flows quite nicely.
But as you read the rhythm goes all **weird** and
Then you find it doesn't even **rhyme** properly
And there's an extra line that shouldn't be there.
And another one.
That's **Disappointillism** – that is.

There are some **fine examples** of Disappointillism
hanging in the Airedale Air Museum. I would recommend
going to see them but, **be warned,** you'll be extremely
disappointed.

Creative writing

The best people to teach you how to do creative writing are those who do creative writing. If your teacher likes **writing stories** too then they can show you how they do it. Lots of authors go into schools and help children with their writing. This is a great idea because they do it for an actual job.

Writing stories was my **favourite** thing to do when I was at school. Here is one I wrote just now.

'Who are you?' asked the lollipop lady.
'I am the Buttery Donkey,' replied the Buttery Donkey.
'What's a buttery donkey?'
'Well, I'm like a normal donkey,' replied the Buttery Donkey.
'But I'm extremely hard to keep hold of. And like a buttery piece of toast, if I fall to the floor, I always land face first on the floor.'
'Right,' said the lollipop lady, 'I'm going home.'

166

When you're little, you sometimes get to spend all day drawing pictures of your **ideas** and writing stories about them. And then, as you get older you start to learn things like beginnings, middles and ends, Story Mountains, editing and planning.

I think everyone should do a little bit of **writing** every day.

At school, your teachers will try and teach you all sorts of **technical** things about writing like subjunctive clauses and punctuation. These are all really important but make sure you get to do some writing that's just fun too. If you're enjoying your writing and you're also reading a nice variety of good books – all that technical stuff will come **naturally.**

Lollipop ladies:
Page 66

Trigonometry

Trigonometry is all about angles and triangles and is a very useful thing to know about. You get to use something called a **protractor.** I like protractors so much that I wrote a poem about them.

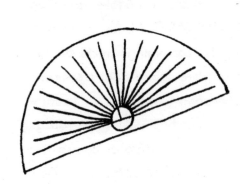 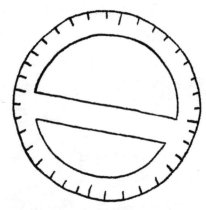

Maths: Page 152

I could **calculate** most of the angles
But some of them I had to **guess.**
Yes I **learned** how to use a protractor
With varying degrees of **success.**

The water cycle

The **water cycle** is just so important and brilliant that everyone loves learning about it. Basically, water falls from the sky as rain, lies around in lakes and puddles and then **evaporates** back into clouds until it gets cold enough to condense back into more rain. And it goes round and round and round.

The **interesting** thing is that even though 70% of the Earth is covered in water, only 2.5% of that water is **fresh.** Only 1% of the water on Earth is **drinkable** and **accessible** and this tiny amount water goes round and round in a cycle keeping all the plants and animals and us alive. Without it we wouldn't last a week. We had probably better look after it then. And tell all the fish to stop **pooing** in it.

You are disgusting!

169

What the flickering pilchard are we going to do about it?

Please help.

It's all very well accepting that we only have one **planet** and that we are using too much of its stuff. But what can you actually do about it? Maybe you could ask your teacher if you and your class could do a school project and come up with loads of **ideas!** Here are some of mine:

Eat less meat:

I love eating meat but it takes up lots of space to grow. It also takes a lot of water and oil. Why not have one day a week when you don't eat any meat at all? Call it **Veggie Saturdays** or something?

VEGGIE SATURDAYS

Walk to school:

Unless you live a long way from school, why not **walk?** Or if you get **driven** to school, why not get your grown-ups to leave twenty minutes earlier, park a mile from the school and you can all walk the rest of the way? Walking to school is really good for you and will put you in a great mood for **learning** by the time you get there.

Don't flush the toilet if it's only yellow:

Every time you **flush** the toilet you are using twelve litres of perfectly good drinking water to flush away something that is completely useful. Maybe the simplest thing you can do is only flush the toilet if you've done a **poo.**

If it's yellow,
Let it mellow.
If it's brown,
Send it down.
If it's blue,
Go to the doctors.
If it's got a face,
Get out of the toilet now!

Art

Art teachers are usually **spattered** with paint and wear floaty **indoor scarves.** They drive old cars and stare out of the window a lot.

Art was one of my **favourite** subjects at school. I wasn't very good at it but that didn't matter. I just used to love sitting around painting and drawing things. I still do actually.

Something that seems to happen a lot in schools is copying works of art by great painters like Van Gogh and his sunflowers and **Matisse and his snail.**

My favourite picture that I ever saw in a primary school was a copy of a **Picasso** painting.

I think the trick with art is always being able to **explain** why you've done something the way you have and pretending that you did it on purpose.

Pasta Picasso: Page 118

Kitchen

There is one place in schools that teachers are not allowed in. It is not their **territory** and if they enter this territory they will have ladles and fish fingers thrown at them. The kitchen is the land of the dinner ladies and no one but dinner ladies can go there.

It is in the **kitchen** that dinner ladies hang out and either cook the school lunches or warm up the lunches that they have been sent from wherever it is they come from.

The kitchen is a noisy place. Everything is **shiny** and there is usually much clattering and banging of saucepans and metal trays. Usually, the kitchen is next to the **school hall** and so if you are doing something in the hall in the hour between break time and lunchtime, you will usually be able to hear the dinner ladies doing their thing.

For some reason, they are not allowed to **quietly** place anything in the sink or on a worktop. Every spoon, ladle and frying pan must be thrown or dropped at huge speed and sound everywhere. The only time dinner ladies quieten down in the kitchen is so they can listen to the quiz on the radio that is playing four times **louder** than a jumbo jet.

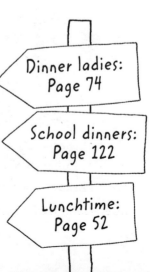

Dinner ladies: Page 74

School dinners: Page 122

Lunchtime: Page 52

Emergencies you might need a banana for

Lots of schools have to put up with the very real problem that **purple monkeys** have invaded and are ruining everything. They are stealing pencils, harassing lollipop ladies and generally causing **mischief.**

Most teachers carry an emergency banana at all times to use as a **distraction** when this happens.

Lollipop ladies:
Page 66

STOP

$\mathcal{S}$imilar **emergencies** happen all the time at school. Some of them involve running out of felt. Others involve a lion being in the playground. Some, however, require a **banana** as their solution.

STOP

Things they don't teach you in school: Page 76

Snacks: Page 26

Problem: You are hungry but it isn't lunchtime yet.

Solution: Eat your emergency banana.

Problem: You are being chased by baddies.

Solution: Eat your emergency banana and then throw the banana skin behind you so the baddies will slip on it.

Problem: You need to phone someone urgently (because there is a lion in the playground).

Solution: Use the banana as a phone.

Problem: You have started to write the word banananananananana and then realised you can't stop.

Solution: Don't bop yourself on the head with a banananananananananananana.

Ouch!

Creative writing: Page 166

Handwriting

When you are at primary school, you will spend a lot of time practising your **handwriting** as a way to help prepare you for living in the **digital age.**

First you learn to **write** each letter on its own. Then you have to start joining them up together so that no one can read what you've written.

I have the **worst** handwriting ever. Here is a sample of my handwriting:

hello, my name is ~~~~~~~~~~~~~ ☺

The reason my handwriting is so bad is that I get very **excited** when I'm writing. My legs start shaking and my elbow bounces up and down. I often find myself **singing** and as the ideas begin to flow through me my writing gets faster and faster and my handwriting gets worse and **worse.**

I think it all started when I was in the **first year** of school.

We would all be doing our handwriting and everyone else would be making **perfect** letters *really* slowly. I would be sitting at the back, doing a kind of dance-writing. I would be making **strange noises** like an out-of-control washing machine and I would be writing so quickly that smoke would be coming out of the end of my pencil. My teacher would come over to me, look at my work and say, 'James, you have written ten times as much as anyone else, but I can't read any of it. You need to slow down and make the letters properly. There is **no point** writing something if no one can read it.'

These days I can write nicely if I really, really try but I don't like it at all. Say it's my mum's birthday and I'm writing her a card: if I go really **slowly,** I can write nicely in the card but it hurts my head. If I'm writing normally, I love it, but it's really **messy.**

So it seems I can either **control** my writing or enjoy my writing but I can't do both at the same time. A bit like quantum physics.

Quantum Physics: Page 82

181

P.E. cupboard

.E. cupboards are **strange** things. They are often quite big – almost as big as a room – but without any windows. Often there is a sign saying that only the P.E. teacher is allowed in there. No one knows what teachers **actually** do in there. Maybe they use it as a base to retreat to in case of some sort of **revolution.**

ortunately, they are usually in the corner of the assembly hall, which is where I spend a lot of time when I visit schools. And so I have spent the last year investigating **P.E. cupboards.** Here is a list of things I have found in them. Some of the things in the list are genuine and others are not.

Can you work out which is which?

Teacher profiles: Page 112

P.E.: Page 188

GENUINE   NOT GENUINE

Basketball

Basketball hoop

Basket case

Chicken in a basket

Box of badminton racquets

Box of squash racquets

Footballs

Cricket balls

Netballs

Rugby balls

Hockey balls

An aircraft carrier

Box of netball bibs

Box of baby bibs

A man called Bob

Some cones

A dead rat

The Charge of the Light Brigade

An asteroid

The Duke of Westminster

A Norfolk lemur

A P.E. teacher having a nap

The answers are not at the back of the book.

How food affects your learning

Yου've probably noticed that if you are finding it hard to **concentrate** at school, your teacher will swoop down on you like a pterodactyl and tell you to stop staring out the window, stop picking your nose, stop yawning and start **paying attention.**

But why do you lose concentration at school? I think that it's often because you haven't eaten enough of the **right things.**

Snacks:
Page 26

Lunchtime:
Page 52

You've probably noticed that if you don't eat enough breakfast, you can't really concentrate at school. When you look at the words on your page or the maths in your book, they all start **bouncing** about and doing jazz dancing in front of your eyes.

And it's the same with **lunch** and all your meals.

I have done a lot of research on this (well, I sat looking at the Internet for an hour and watched some videos on YouTube) and apparently, children who eat **healthily** do much better at school than children who don't eat healthily.

So, if want to **do well** at school make sure that all of your meals include some of the following things:

Fruit, Vegetables, Grains, Dairy, Catapults, Protein
(One of those might not be true)

Examples of healthy food might include:

1. A beef burger in a wholegrain bun with some broccoli and a glass of milk.

2. Your own very delicious homemade granola.

Making your own **granola** is a cheap fun way of creating a really healthy breakfast that will set you up for a great day of learning.

Ingredients include, lots of **rolled oats** and all the nuts, seeds and dried fruit that you like. Mix it all together and keep in an **airtight container** – your grown-up will help you find one.

When you're ready for your **breakfast,** simply chuck loads into your cereal bowl and cover it in milk or fruit juice. You might want to put a **dollop** of yoghurt on the top. Maybe even some maple syrup.

Different sizes of cow: Page 60

School council: Page 56

School dinners: Page 122

Granola is full of **good stuff** that will stop from you being **hungry** all morning and it will give you lots of brain food for school.

If your brain is **hungry** it can only think in circles. If you can't think, how are you supposed to learn anything?

The other thing to do is **avoid** food with lots of **sugar** in them. I don't eat sugar at all. All it does is seem to make me want to eat more sugar. What's **the point** of food that makes you hungry? You wouldn't drink a drink that made you want to drink more of it, would you? Or wear clothes that made you cold? Or read a book that made you know **less?**

But seriously, get your food right and your grades will **improve.** It's a scientific **fact!**

P.E.

For some reason, the **running around** you do at break time isn't enough to keep you fit and healthy. No – you must also be subjected to something called **P.E.**

P.E. stands for Physical Education but that's too **complicated** for most P.E. teachers to remember so they just call it P.E. Some schools call it Games or Sports or Gym or Running Round In Your Pants.

P.E. teachers will usually want to time you or measure something. They will want you to go faster, further or stronger. Try to humour them as they often live alone and spend most of their time binge-watching **bad telly** while getting slower, weaker and floppier.

If you're lucky, your school will have strange gym **equipment** in the hall, which swings out and gets locked into place so that you can spend an hour **failing** to climb up a rope.

There will also be piles of blue mats that smell **fantastic** and allow you to fall off things without **hurting** yourself as much as if there were no mats.

Some schools don't have **mats.** They have pools of lava, infested with **sharks.**

It's your **responsibility** to make sure you have your P.E. kit on the right day. If you forget to bring your P.E. kit to school the worst thing in the world will happen to you. You will have to wear the spare P.E. kit. This looks like a normal P.E. kit but smells of other children and feels scratchy and **nasty.**

Avoid this at all costs.

P.E. cupboard:
Page 182

Catapulting
to school:
Page 134

Sports day:
Page 88

FINANCIAL
TIMES

What teachers do when you're not there

Once, when I was at school, I fell **asleep** at my desk in a maths lesson about imaginary numbers. For some reason, no one bothered to wake me up and when I did wake up it was half past eleven at night. What was really **surprising** was that my maths teacher was wearing his pyjamas and dancing the **tango** with one of the P.E. teachers.

I still have **nightmares** about this.

Obviously, everyone knows that when you go home from school, most teachers stay in the building and sleep in a cupboard on a **nest** made from lost school uniforms and **felt.**

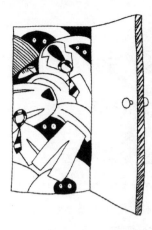

But they can't be **sleeping** all the time.

I did a **survey** and asked 400 teachers what they did when they had the classroom to themselves and these were the results:

I roll around on the carpet area **giggling** to myself – **4%**

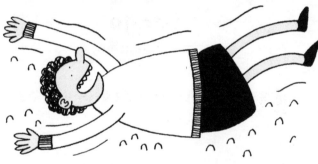

I eat a **massive** cake – **5%**

I write lists of things I would be doing if I weren't a teacher – **10%**

I mark your homework – **40%**

I make up lesson plans – **30%**

I download lesson plans from the Internet and pretend I made them up myself – **47%**

I cast spells – **3%**

I go on YouTube and watch videos of cats falling off things – **87%**

I pick my bogies and label them – **13%**

I add up all the percentages in surveys to check that they make 100 – **124%**

Carpet area:
Page 89

194

Being poorly at school

If you're poorly at school, you have to **convince** your teacher you really **are** poorly and that you're not just trying to get out of class.

This afternoon we are all going to do a maths test.

I have the plague.

Some illnesses are **worse** than others in a school. If it's just a cold, teachers may expect you to ignore it and carry on regardless.

If you get the **vomiting** bug, however, you will find that everyone wants you to go home immediately.

Releasing deadly **bottom burps** is quite a good way to get sent home. No one wants a **farter** in the classroom.

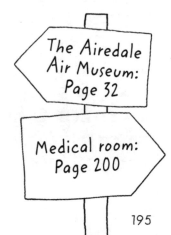

The Airedale Air Museum: Page 32

Medical room: Page 200

Things that were normal for your parents

'When I was your age,' your dad says, 'we didn't have mobile phones. If I wanted to phone my friend I had to go to the **phone box** at the end of the road and put money in it!'

Here are some other things that were different when your parents were little but are just **weird** now. Some of them are more than weird, they are just plain **crazy.**

Paste sandwiches

Rather than eat real food, your parents ate something called **paste.** It came in a jar and was available in flavours like beef, fish and cat. It didn't have any nutritional value but was just supposed to make bread more **interesting.** It was really **cheap** and tasted of goldfish and **vomit**

PASTES

Milk breaks

Up until 1978, school children had a **break** for a glass of milk in the morning. This gave them much-needed vitamins and calcium. And made some of them **sick.**

Cars with no seat belts in the back

For some reason it took a while to realise that it might be a good idea if children wore **seat belts** in cars. It was only in 1986 that it became the law for car manufacturers to put them in their cars. And it was only made law that you actually had to use seat belts in 1991. Until then children just used to slide around the back seat especially if their grown-up went really **fast** around a corner.

No car seats for babies

When I was seven, my baby brother was born and when we went in the car, he just laid down in a **carry cot** (which was basically a cardboard box covered in material) on the back seat. It was my job to sit next to the carry cot and hold on to it in case we had to brake **quickly.**

Parents' evening

Once or twice a year, teachers are supposed to let your grown-ups ask **questions** about how you're getting on. This is always **awkward** for everyone.

It's **awkward** for children because every day for a year when your mum asks you 'What did you do at school?' You shrugged and groaned and said, 'Nothing.' But on parents' evening they will actually find out that you have been studying the **ancient Egyptians.** And that you really **enjoyed** it.

It's **awful** for parents. They listen to your teacher telling them about you and realise you are a slightly **different** person at school.

It's **awful** for teachers too. They have to tidy the classroom, stay at work **late** and remember all their children's names.

Is he?

Manuel is such a polite little boy.

Medical room

When teachers get **poorly** they go into a special bio-pod in the corner of the classroom. It looks a bit like a tiny **spaceship** and they simply lie in there while various robots and computer programmes rebuild the tissues of whatever is wrong with them.

But if you get poorly you have to go to the **medical room!**

Trust me, you don't want to end up here unless you really can't help it. There are never any windows and there's usually a pile of papier mâché sick bowls which make you want to be **sick** just looking at them.

When I was little, if I was feeling sick, my mum would always give me a **mixing bowl** to be sick in. And the mixing bowl would always remind me of raw cake mixture – the thought of which would make me **sick.** Similarly, I really enjoyed eating my mum's homemade **cakes,** but they would always make me feel a little bit sick for some reason.

The same thing happens with the **medical room.** As soon as you sit in one, you feel poorly. If you want to avoid being poorly – **avoid** the medical room.

Being poorly at school: Page 195

If you are **poorly** already though, the medical room is a great place to be sick, faint, come out in spots and go yellow. Try it some time. There isn't a lot to look at in the medical room. Usually just a bed covered in **itchy** green paper. If you're really lucky there might be a nurse or a matron or a teacher who once did some first aid training and is really hoping that your parents come to pick you up before you are sick in her **hair.**

Allergy children: Page 86

Accidents at school: Page 202

Accidents at school

The other day, one of my children – the one called Hayden – came home from school with an accident report sheet from his teacher explaining that at break time he had fallen over a twig. Not even a stick. It was a **twig.**

School is clearly a health and safety **nightmare!**

Here are some things that you should watch out for at school:

Bumping into someone in the corridor

Running into a climbing frame

Getting hit in the face with a football

Getting hit in the side of the head with a dodgy badminton racquet

Food poisoning

Fire

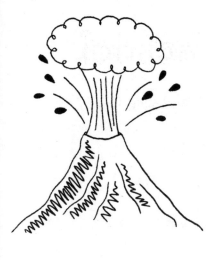

Flood

Volcanic eruption

Other sorts of eruption (ie: chicken)

Being bopped on the bottom by a mad lollipop lady

Felt burn

Slipping on someone else's emergency banana skin

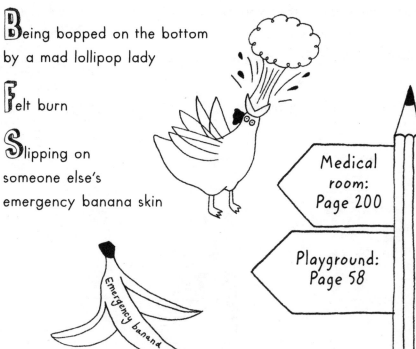

Medical room: Page 200

Playground: Page 58

Emergency banana

Things that shouldn't be in this book

Alice in Wonderland

This is definitely one of my **favourite** books and Lewis Carroll is one of my favourite authors but it hasn't really got anything to do with teachers. I think Lewis Carroll was a kind of **teacher** at Oxford University but he spent most of his time writing mathematical problems and brilliant stories for young people.

How to milk a hamster

On page something or other, I wrote about how different sizes of **cows** can be milked to make different **strengths** of milk. I suggest that there are cows that are the size of a hamster. You have probably been wondering how on earth you would milk such a **tiny creature**. Well, the answer is to use a pair of tweezers and lots and lots of **patience.**

hamster

Different sizes of cow: Page 60

You might also like:

THE FUNNY LIFE OF PETS

Uncover **side-splittingly** funny facts all about **pets** and **prepare yourself** for a knee-slappingly, snot-inducingly and stomach-achingly **hilarious** read!

What happens when you **fart** in a dog's face? What does your pet do when you're not home? And why are **cats** so **afraid** of **cucumbers?**

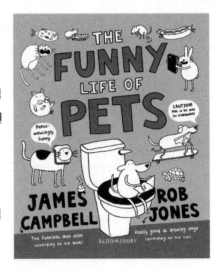

'I loved *The Funny Life of Pets*. It's funny AND sarcastic.'

Noah, aged 9

Dynamic duo **James Campbell** (funniest man alive – according to his mum) and **Rob Jones** (good at drawing dogs – according to his cat) answer all these questions and more in the eye-wateringly uproarious **The Funny Life of Pets.**

Fact ⚠ WARNING ⚠ WARNING ⚠ Fact

Fact ⚠ WARNING ⚠ WARNING ⚠ Fact

Fact Alert

Fact Alert

Anything you think you might learn from this book might not be very accurate so should not be used in a school project or as part of your homework. Unless, of course, you are made of stardust and are as brave as sunshine.

The last page of the book

This is the **last** page of the book. Well done for finding it.

We were going to show you a picture of a naked teacher but it was just too **terrifying** so here is a picture of a naked school **hamster** instead.

Congratulations on finding the **end** of the book. Why not go back to the first page and start again. You might have missed something terribly **unimportant.**

Beginning page:
Page 10